NEW TALL TALES
OF
Pecos Bill

NEW TALL TALES

OF

Pecos Bill

by

HAROLD W. FELTON

ILLUSTRATED BY WILLIAM MOYERS

8166

Prentice-Hall, Inc., Englewood Cliffs, N. J.

398.2

For Mandy

The Truth About Pecos Bill

THE WHOLE world has heard of the exploits and adventures of Pecos Bill, that mighty hero of the Old West. Everyone knows of his invention of the cowpunching business, the six-gun, and the lariat. The world knows, too, how Bill rode and broke a cyclone. But there are many new tales about Pecos Bill that have never been told before.

New and heretofore unknown incidents in the life of Pecos Bill have recently come to light. Most important by far to admirers of the hero are the disclosures made by Three-fingered Ike. Ike possessed intimate knowledge of Bill's early life. Knowledge of the old days before Pecos fell out of a westward-bound wagon on the banks of the Pecos River, hit a rock, broke the rock, bruised his head, lost his memory, and became a coyote.

Everyone knows how Bill cut his teeth on a bowie knife. That fact and Bill's fight with Rat, the big rattlesnake, and Scat, the ferocious mountain lion, are matters of history. He tamed and rode the cougar. Just to make it a fair fight, he gave the rattler the first three bites and, after he whipped him, used the snake for a quirt.

And certainly everyone must know how Pecos Bill captured the Great Pacing White Mustang of the Plains, and how that beautiful palomino became his famous mount and friend, known far and wide as Widow Maker.

Everyone knows how Pecos Bill fought dangerous Gun Smith, one of the fastest gun slingers in the West. After that breathtaking duel, Bill took over Hell's Gate Gulch ranch and made Gun Smith his foreman.

Hell's Gate Gulch! That was Bill's home ranch. His first ranch. Where he met the rootin'-tootin' *hombres* he taught how to be cowpunchers. Curly Joe, the hoss wrangler. Mushmouth, who played the mouth organ. Bullfrog Doyle. Pretty Pete Rogers. Bronco Jones. Alkali Ike. Bean Hole, the cook. Rip-snortin' buckaroos, every one.

Patient research has revealed new adventures of

the greatest of all cowpunchers. Adventures that
show how truly remarkable Pecos Bill was. Where
all men were big, Pecos was the biggest. His horse
could run faster and jump higher than any other.
His ideas were the greatest. His own buckaroos
served him with fierce loyalty. His enemies hated
him with trickery and violence.

Any information about the first and greatest
cowpuncher is important. But these revelations of
Three-fingered Ike are especially notable because
they supply information of the early years, the childhood days, when the seeds of personality are planted
and the foundation of character is formed.

In the West, in Pecos Bill's West, the geography
was rough. The landscape was hard. Even the
weather was violent. Wild animals, dangerous creatures were everywhere. Trees and bushes, gentle
and friendly elsewhere, were armed with thorns.
The men who lived in such a land, faced it with the
roughness and violence necessary to continue to live.
Little wonder their justice was violent too.

Pecos Bill spent most of his life packing a pair of
six-guns for the law. But he did more than that. His
influence developed and spread simple courtesy.
When he was around, most of the bad men were
models of politeness. Bill was a gentle, peaceful man,
and a good shot. But he was quick-tempered, too.

The bad men knew these things and tried not to offend him.

It wasn't always easy. The worst of the bad men, like the land they lived in, were likely to be rugged and tough. It often took two or three shots to kill them. And posses sometimes had a good deal of trouble in hanging a horse thief. They had to hang much longer than in the East.

The fight with the lawless seemed sometimes to be never-ending. Pecos did it as gently as circumstances permitted. There was not always loss of life. Far from it. Many times he could stop a bad man by shooting his trigger finger off. Often, the loss was nothing more than a few front teeth. He used no more force than was absolutely necessary.

The conservative nature of the following biographical material will not be unnoticed by Pecos Bill devotees and scholars. It is an important point. It would not be difficult to surrender occasionally to a temptation to exaggerate. But Bill himself was always a stickler for the truth. That alone is sufficient reason to avoid repeating rumors and unfounded, unverified reports. To spread the blanket, even in the slightest, would do little more than invite controversy. As Pecos Bill avoided controversy, so do his admirers.

There is a great and overwhelming fact about

Pecos Bill that goes far, far beyond the mere telling of some of his adventures. Bill was big. Every statement as to his size may be accepted as the precise truth because it is a simple fact that Pecos Bill was too big to lie about.

He had courage to match his size. It was something like the courage of other men. But there was more of it. He had more strength, too. He not only had strength and courage for himself, he had enough for others. With him, it was catching. Even now, anyone can draw on Pecos Bill's courage and strength whenever he likes. And his ability, and imagination, too. He had enough for everyone.

Harold W. Felton

Contents

NEW TALL TALES
OF
Pecos Bill

A Tale of a Dog's Tail

EVERYONE knows about Pecos Bill's bowie knife. It was so sharp he could shave himself with its shadow. When he knew he was going to be in a hurry in the morning, he often saved time by putting it under his pillow, or the rolled-up slicker he used for a pillow when he was on the range. During the night, the bowie knife shaved him slick as a whistle.

But very few people know how the bowie knife played a part in a strange adventure at the foot of Mount San Jacinto, when Pecos Bill camped there with Three-fingered Ike. It was a pleasant place. The mountain towered above to the southwest and an arm of the sea stretched up between the San Jacinto and the Little San Bernardino Mountains.

The fact that a desert now occupies the place merely supplies an added element of curiosity to a curious tale. It was Pecos Bill who planted the date palms that still mark the place. It was he who first discovered the warm, sulphur springs. And it was he who gave the name of Palm Springs to the locality the Indians had previously called *Agua Caliente,* a Spanish phrase, which, as everyone should know, means hot water.

Pecos Bill wasn't looking for any special trouble. Of course, you don't have to look for trouble to find it. He was on a little exploring trip. He was thinking of using Southern California for a calf pasture and wanted to see whether it would do or not. Three-fingered Ike had come along to keep him company, and there wasn't any better company on the trail.

Three-fingered Ike was a fine old cowpuncher, who had joined the Hell's Gate Gulch outfit soon after Bill organized it. Bill had liked him from the beginning. It was easy to see that Ike was the soul of honesty. He was a cowpoke of great ability and a man of character who could be depended on when the going was rough.

The first night out, Bill ran down an antelope and dressed it while Three-fingered Ike built a fire and prepared a camp.

When he finished with his bowie knife, Bill threw

it at a nearby date palm. The blade sank deep into the wood. But instead of coming to a quivering halt, the bowie knife kept right on cutting. It cut a hole through the tree trunk and would have fallen to the ground without incident, except for a simple fact. That fact was that Norther, Bill's dog, was sleeping on the other side of the tree. When the bowie knife fell, it did not fall harmlessly on the ground. It fell harmfully on Norther's tail. The result was that the long, close relationship between Norther and his tail ended.

It didn't seem to hurt him. The knife was sharp and the cut was clean and complete. It must have been a sensation something like an annoying flea. For Norther turned as if to stop an annoyance of that sort. The usual sharp, brisk nibbling on the portion of his tail that seemed to offend brought no result. It seemed as though he couldn't feel his sharp teeth scratching along his tailbone. He got up to circle around, in an effort to do a better job. But strangely, to him at least, his tail didn't get up with him. It took only a moment's consideration to bring the awful truth home to the surprised dog. There had been no cry of distress or pain. So it is probable that the howls that followed were howls of surprise.

Bill looked at his unfortunate dog. Something must be done. Norther needed his tail. It was a good tail. But even if it were no more than an ordinary tail, Norther must have it. He must have it to chase, if nothing else.

There were esthetics to be considered, too. Norther was the only dog in the world that could wag his tail up and down. Bill taught him to do that once when they were hunting mavericks in the Narrow Canyon Country. They were constantly working in narrow canyons. The canyon walls were so close together the poor dog couldn't wag his tail from side to side in the conventional way. He couldn't complete a full, dog-sized wag for each movement of his tail was abruptly stopped by the sheer rock walls on either side.

The natural result, of course, was a very, very sore tail, and a consequent lack of desire to wag. It was clear to Norther that in a test of wearing qualities between solid rock and a dog's tail, that the latter would prove less durable.

Norther had always been a happy dog. He showed his pleasant disposition in the way common to happy dogs, by wagging his tail. But when the canyons kept him from wagging, he became silent and sad, and had no joy in the hunt for the mavericks. It was then that Bill taught him to wag up and down. The dog learned rapidly. His sunny nature returned and once again he sniffed up and down the narrow canyons, wagging his tail up and down, and never touching the rocky walls at the side. Little wonder Pecos Bill took a personal pride in that tail!

While all scholars do not agree, there is substantial evidence that it was Pecos Bill who first said: "The reason why a dog is called man's best friend is because he wags his tail instead of his tongue." The only man who ever taught a dog to wag up and down was certainly the man who must have invented this well-known saying.

All in all, Norther's tail was important, not only to him, but to Pecos Bill. Something must be done about it. Norther could not go through life without a tail.

Three-fingered Ike was helpful. "How about this?" he said. "We got a jug of sourdough. We kin put some sourdough around the cut place. We kin fasten the tail to the dog, an' wrap it up good an' tight. Won't be no time at all 'til that tail is as good as new."

Bill brightened. "That's right. That's a good idea. That sourdough kin cure anything. I remember how it healed Curly Joe that time Widow Maker throwed him."

"Shore," said Ike. "An' it's jest as good fer the outside of a man as it is fer the inside. Don't see no reason why it won't work on a dog."

He brought the sourdough jug. Bill applied it liberally and carefully bound tail and dog together with a strip of gunny sack. He tied the burlap on good and tight with a couple of pigging strings.

Ike smiled with approval. He had great faith in the healing power of the famous sourdough. When the operation was finished, Bill stood up, pleased with his work. Everyone was pleased. If Norther had shown his pleasure with a smile everything might have been all right. But he didn't. He showed his emotion in a more dog-like manner. He wagged his tail.

Powerful as the famous sourdough was, it could not prevail against such odds. At the end of the second wag, the bandage slipped and the tail went flying through the air into a bunch of tumbleweeds and sandburrs.

Pecos retrieved the tail. Norther was a great retriever, but he did not seem inspired to go chasing through a sandburr patch to fetch his own tail. Bill removed the burrs and the needles and brushed off the sand. "Look here," he said to the dog, "if you don't hold still, here is goin' to be the end of your tail."

He performed the operation again, and again Norther promptly wagged his tail off. But still Bill didn't give up. He put the tail in a sling. But after several futile attempts, he was forced to admit defeat.

"Mighty strange," he said to Ike. "It's real peculiar. Here I taught that dog to wag up an' down. I even taught him to wag in circles. But somehow I jest cain't seem to teach him to stop waggin'."

Ike was sad. He knew Bean Hole, the cook, would be heartbroken when he heard the news. It was the first time a sourdough cure had ever failed. It was another one of the few occasions Pecos Bill met with failure. But it seemed to be inevitable. Norther was without a tail and seemed destined to remain in that unfortunate state.

"Guess there ain't nothin' more we kin do," Bill said sadly.

"Nope," Ike agreed. "We done all we kin."

"Then let's clean up around here," Bill said.

Ike unknotted the pigging strings as Bill tossed the messy gunny sack into the fire. "What are we goin' to do with Norther?" he asked, half to himself.

"What do you mean?" Ike inquired.

"The pore dog is bloody. We ought to clean him up."

"Wash a dog?" Ike exclaimed in amazement.

"I know what to do. I'll jest run him in the crick here below the warm sulphur springs," Bill said. "The water is healin'. He looks a little pale after losin' his tail, an' havin' all them operations an' all. It will do him good. And he'll splash around in the water, and come out clean, too."

Pecos picked up a stick and threw it into the stream that flowed slowly away from the warm springs toward the inland sea. Norther jumped into the water with a splash. He swam to the stick, took it in his mouth and returned to shore. He shook himself as he emerged from the water, and the spray filled the air. After this brief pause, he bounded toward Pecos and dropped the stick at his feet.

But Bill did not see the stick. His eyes were firmly fixed on the south end of Norther. His steady, unflinching gaze demanded Ike's attention.

"Boss!" Ike shouted. "Bill! Look!" No more words would come from the surprised man's mouth. There was no need for more. His finger pointed at Norther's tail. Not the place where the tail had been. Not at a vacant space at the end of the dog. Not at a stub. But at a tail, a full-grown, life-sized tail! And it was wagging, wagging as only the tail of a happy dog can wag!

"Wha . . . wha . . . what done it?" Ike demanded weakly.

"Let's figger this thing out," Bill said quietly and slowly. The famous poker face did not reveal the surprise he felt.

"How . . . how . . . did it happen?" Ike asked.

Bill examined the new tail. "It's on good an' solid," he said. "You cain't even see where it's fastened on."

"But . . . but . . ."

"Only thing I kin see is that a new tail growed on because the water is so powerful an' healin'. I knowed it was real good water, but I didn't know it was good enough to grow a new tail on a dog."

The new tail was full-grown and beautiful. More beautiful than the old one, for it had never been bruised by the walls of narrow canyons. This tail had never been raked by cactus needles or loaded down with sandburrs. This fine, new tail had never even been chased. But for all its newness and beauty, it had all the skill of the old tail. Norther had perfect control. He wagged it back and forth, up and down, and in circles.

Bill was overjoyed. Ike forgot for the moment the failure of the sourdough. Norther, delighted with his new posterior extremity, chased it. He was completely happy. It chased fine. Just like the old one.

Pecos was putting two and two together. A dog and a new tail had somehow been put together. Perhaps even more startling things were possible.

There is no way of knowing how a lesser man would have acted. But Pecos Bill acted decisively and promptly. He stooped and picked up the matted and abused tail that had just been through so many unsuccessful tail-rending operations. It was a wretched tail. A lifeless thing. Indeed, in the light of its recent unfortunate experiences, it could scarcely be expected to be otherwise.

Bill held it in his hand for a moment. Norther pricked up his ears, and danced about, barking eagerly as he always did while waiting for a stick to be thrown. A sharp movement of the arm and the amputated tail sped through the air toward the stream. Norther bounded after it, now eager to retrieve anything thrown by his master.

It apparently made not the slightest difference to him that it once was a part of him. His constant companion. His bosom companion in all respects, except for its former physical location. Pecos Bill had held it like a stick. It looked like a stick. At least, something like a stick. It had been thrown as sticks are thrown for dogs to fetch. And he would treat it like a stick. He would fetch it.

His former pride and joy hit the water with a splash. Bill had thrown it far downstream. Norther went racing toward the bank, barking a joyful chorus of barks. The graceful leap into the water was approaching. But instead of the plunge, Norther broke his running stride and with a scurry of feet, managed to stop at the water's edge.

Norther had chased many sticks. He knew that a stick floats in water. A tail might do that. Or it might sink. He would not have been surprised in either case. But the tail neither floated nor sank. It seemed to continue to splash. Not just a light skip or two on the surface of the water. It splashed. And the splashes didn't stop. They grew and continued to grow. No one could be quite sure what was happening. No one could be quite sure how it happened. The spray and the turmoil in the water prevented that.

The splashing died down. Something was there. It was coming toward shore. Swimming. In the short time it took to swim to the creek bank, Pecos approached. His hands seemed to be moving freely and naturally, but they hovered near his six guns. No telling what might happen. Ike stood quite still, his eyes and mouth wide open.

Whatever it was, it gained the bank and came out of the water. It turned around three times in lowering and tightening circles. It came to rest on the side of its rump, pivoted easily to a hip bone, and industriously scratched an ear with the free hind leg.

"It looks like a dog!" said Bill.

It shook itself. The spray rose and fell.

"It acts like a dog!"

It made a sound. A pleasant, familiar sound, "Woof."

"It barks like a dog!"

It approached Norther. Norther approached it.

"It sniffs like a dog!" Pecos Bill observed.

Norther turned to Bill and touched the big cowpuncher's hand. The new arrival also turned to Bill. Pecos Bill felt a cold nose on his knuckles. He felt a soft, warm tongue lick his fingers affectionately.

Pecos Bill crouched down. He ran his hands over the newcomer's face and ears. He saw big, devoted eyes gazing into his own. He saw a pink tongue reach out playfully in an attempt to lick his face.

"By golly!" Bill said. "It *is* a dog!" He turned back to Ike, whose eyes and mouth were still open, unable to squint or pucker, even to express disbelief. But

Bill knew there would be questions. He might just
as well settle everything right now. He put his hand
on Ike's shoulder. Gently, softly, he explained.

"That water is jest that healin' an' healthful, that's
all. There probably ain't no limit to what that water
kin do. There probably ain't nothin' it won't grow.
First Norther went in it, an' it growed a new tail on
him. Then, I throwed that ole tail in that water, an'
it growed a new dog on it."

Ike was silent for several hours. Seemed like he
had something on his mind. He left his supper almost
untouched. For the most part he sat, staring vacantly
into the distance. But occasionally he would shake
his head, trying to force his mind back to reality, and
his eyes back into focus. When he did, his eyes
sought out the same object, the new dog.

It *was* a dog. There was no doubt about it. And
quite like Norther, too. There were, however, some
differences. And the differences, in many respects,
were quite pronounced. While Norther was an old
dog with a new tail, the newcomer was a new dog
with an old tail.

Pecos Bill had an opportunity to satisfy himself as
to a problem that had troubled him ever since his
experience with Norther in the Narrow Canyon
Country. He had wondered whether he had edu-
cated the tail, or the dog. Now was the time to find

out. Norther's new tail could wag in all directions. Not so in the other case. In fact, Pecos discovered, much to his surprise, that instead of the dog wagging the tail, it was the tail that wagged the dog. And only sideways.

Bill was about to formulate an immutable law for the benefit of scientists who might have cause to consider the problem in the future. It seemed that an old tail retained its natural, hereditary characteristics; that when it was cut off, it was cut off from abilities previously learned. Moreover, while it is well known that you can't teach an old dog new tricks, it is equally true that you cannot teach an old tail new tricks.

At that moment, Bill's scientific studies were halted. Norther started to chase his tail. The other dog would not be outdone. He started to do the same thing. But the result was confusing, for the tail began to chase the dog. Here was an apparent exception to the rule. At least, it was something that required further study.

Pecos did not like exceptions to rules and he was somewhat relieved when the dog, tired of being chased, lay down. But there were new fascinations in store. For instead of repose, he was presented with a new, unusual sight. Instead of a stretched-out dog, with an idly wagging tail bumping against the earth, here was a tail in repose with a wagging dog bumping up and down on the ground.

A ground-thumping tail never seems to bother a dog. But the new, ground-thumping dog, while it didn't seem to bother the tail, certainly bothered the dog.

Emotionally and physically, he had a very difficult time for a while. When he was in good spirits, or when he was trying to show he was friendly, in common with all dogs, he wagged. After he had banged himself down on the ground a few times, he lost his good spirits as well as the fine feeling of friendship that had started his punishment. No longer having anything to be happy about, he stopped wagging. Then the abuse ceased. He was a smart dog, and he soon discovered the way to avoid being hurt by a hard floor was not to wag at all.

He learned so fast that few people ever saw it happen. That, in certain respects, is unfortunate because there is a marked tendency in certain cynical circles to deprecate the whole story, simply because not many people saw it happen. Luckily, however, the eyewitnesses were men of repute. Their testimony, well buttressed by reputations for keen observation and character above reproach, permits us to know the truth.

In the course of time, Ike regained the use of his

vocal chords. "What are you goin' to name that-there new dog?" he asked.

Pecos did not hesitate. "Souther," he said. The reply was immediate, spontaneous. Here was greatness in action. The right word at the right time. Every student of Pecos Bill will recall that Norther was named with a similar flash of genius. The ordinary man names his dog after labored consideration of a list including Fido, Rover, Shep. Not so, Pecos Bill.

Norther had been named right. If the opposite of North is South, certainly and clearly, the other end of Norther must be Souther.

Jumping
the Grand Canyon

PECOS BILL and Widow Maker were an ideal pair. No man and horse were ever more suited to each other. Bill required strict obedience. Widow Maker gave it willingly. Quick response to command is essential where delay may mean death.

On the other hand, Bill knew his great pacing mustang possessed a keen animal intelligence. An instinct that no man could ever equal. Not even the first and greatest of cowpunchers. No man could understand. Not even Pecos Bill himself. And a cowboy knows that often his pony's instinct can save him when nothing else can.

The mutual confidence that existed between Widow Maker and Pecos was born at the time of the great bucking contest that resulted in the horse's capture. The world's greatest bucking exhibition, it has often been called, with justice. The confidence was never broken, nor even bent, during all the adventures arising from the invention of ranching and the taming of the West. In fact, each dangerous experience they shared tempered it with respect and admiration, and made it even stronger.

Consider the time Widow Maker tried to jump the Grand Canyon. He made the jump at Bill's command. It was all the result of carelessness, of course. Plain thoughtlessness. Both characteristics that do not figure large in a Pecos Bill biography. But Bill probably got to thinking Widow Maker could jump anything, so in a moment of exuberance during a fast ride along the rim of the canyon, he turned the horse suddenly and headed directly toward the chasm.

Widow Maker didn't hesitate. He took the jump. He gave a powerful leap and shot up and through the air!

Pecos Bill's mind was so lost in the speed, and the rhythm of the hoofbeats drumming beneath him, and the smooth, rolling motion of the ride, that he really didn't think of the consequences. That was unusual because the big cowpuncher rarely made mistakes. When he did, they were likely to be important.

They had been jumping canyons most of the morning and Pecos had become accustomed to the long break in the rhythm of pounding hoofs as the palomino soared through space. Always the heady intoxication of the leap had been broken by the thunder of hoofs when the mustang landed on the opposite side. But this time, the end of the flight seemed long in coming. Where was the heavy thud of sharp hoofs?

The long silence brought Bill's mind back to reality. It was a long, eerie pause. It was a pause broken at last, not by the thunder of hoofs, but by a sharp squeak of saddle leather as the pacing mustang's muscles strove to overcome the obstacles of empty space and the law of gravity.

Where were they? Why was the roar of hammering hoofs so long in coming? He looked around. Now his senses returned. Now the sharp grey eyes missed not a thing. And his eyes did not see the vast blueness of the open sky far above the surface of the earth. They met instead the grim, cold walls of the canyon. He had fallen below the rim. The blue sky was far above. It was too late.

There was no chance of landing on the mesa on the opposite side. That chance was gone. Irretrievably gone! They were going down. Down to the rocky bottom. Already they had fallen below the

small peaks that struggled upward from the floor of the canyon. Each split second brought them nearer to doom. The situation was desperate.

But now Pecos Bill was alert. Alert to the danger and ready to meet it. There was only one chance. Only one hope. And it was based on the absolute, immediate obedience of the Great Pacing White Mustang!

The palomino had accepted the command to jump without hesitation. Without question. His unswerving obedience had brought them face to face with the present desperate predicament. The mustang now had good reason to be suspicious of Bill's command. Pecos was painfully aware of that. His awareness increased as the rocks below came rushing toward the falling pair.

The foolish, ill-advised command to jump had brought them to the door of doom. Pecos did not despair. His knees gripped the saddle. He tightened the reins.

The rocky bottom of the canyon was flying toward them. Man and horse plunged down past the tops of the tallest towering pines. Down, past the tops of the lower-growing deciduous trees. Down. Down past the tops of the bushes and the brush. Down. Down, almost to the tops of the low cactus.

Now, if ever, was the time. In another small fraction of a second, it would be too late!

Pecos leaned forward. The fluttering silver mane lashed his face. His back and legs stiffened. The muscles of his arms grew taut. It was time! He acted. He gave the command. "Whoa!"

His voice was calm, but firm. There was no denying such a command. The big palomino obeyed. Instantly. He stopped, sliding to an abrupt stop, scarcely a foot above the cruel, jagged rocks.

Bill released his grip on the reins. As the slack came to the leather, the big cowpuncher's steel muscles relaxed. He swung himself down out of the saddle. Carefully he led Widow Maker the short step down to the jagged rocks that so recently threatened to destroy them. Then over the rocks, and down to the soft, solid earth. Bill's first thought was always for the welfare of his horse and he took great pains to protect his feet from injury on the sharp stones.

They moved silently to the cool shade of trees growing at the base of the rock wall. There Bill turned and slid his wide-brimmed hat off the back of his head. He looked up at the canyon's rim on the opposite side. His other hand ran up his mustang's neck, through the luxurious silver-white mane. It came to rest on the soft, golden muzzle.

"Pardner," said Pecos Bill, "that was a close one."

Neither Widow Maker nor Pecos accepted defeat easily. Both of them should have known that some things, including the Grand Canyon, are too big to jump. Both of them should have known that the recovery of a fumble is not defeat at all, but success. But Bill was a believer in simple, direct action. To him, a goal was a goal. When he started anything, he finished it. There was an unspoken understanding between man and horse that a new goal existed. To jump the Grand Canyon!

Whenever the opportunity presented itself, jumping was the order of the day. They eagerly accepted every opportunity for practice. It was still a good sport. The thrill and the excitement remained in the soaring leaps. But beneath it was a very real seriousness of purpose. To jump the Grand Canyon.

They jumped gullies, arroyos, canyons, deep canyons, small canyons, large canyons, wide canyons. The goal remained the same. To jump the Grand Canyon.

No words were spoken. There was no bravado. No threats. No boasting. There was a job to do and both of them knew what that job was.

Time passed and Bill continued the never-ending business of inventing the great inventions that were to bring the cow business to its present state of perfection. But the memory of the failure to jump the Grand Canyon remained. Then the day came. It seemed to come by accident. Pecos Bill, astride Widow Maker, was again approaching the very spot where the yawning chasm had defeated them.

Widow Maker's sharp ears pointed forward. He was ready to try again. The ears fell back as if eagerly waiting for a new command. The welcome words came. The sound of the hoofs on the rocky plateau quickened. Pecos leaned forward, tightened the reins and pressed his heels to the mustang's ribs.

The Great White Mustang broke into the pacing gait for which he was famous. Faster and faster.

Straight for the vast emptiness that filled the world between two sheer rock walls. Straight for the great gulf between the mountains, worn deep and wide by water and by time and by the force of countless convulsions of nature.

He was going at breakneck speed. His silver mane danced back, whipping his rider's face. His long, white tail stretched out straight, above and always ahead of the rocks thrown up by the flashing hoofs.

The canyon's edge approached. If either Pecos Bill or Widow Maker had misgivings, it was too late to stop now. It was too late to turn aside. The jump had to be made!

There was no excited clatter of nervous hoofs in preparation for the leap. There was the steady, firm rhythm. There was a final crash of hard hoofs on rock. Then there was silence. The silence of empty space as horse and rider soared up and through the air.

Up! Up! Through the air. Up, and up. Bill was alert every instant. Widow Maker had done his best. And his best was perfect. Or so it seemed. If they failed this time, it would not be due to lack of determination. Nor would it be due to lighthearted preparation. It would only be because the Grand Canyon was too big for them.

The jump was going well. It was going fine. Fine!

They were a quarter of the way across. And they were still going up. They were a third of the way across. The cold wind whistled past them. They were reaching the top of the jump. If they could pass the halfway mark . . . in a few seconds they would know.

Bill's eyes and senses were dancing. Now the flying pair was leveling off. It would be close, but they would make it! The top of the giant arc had been reached. Now they would glide down to the opposite side, safe! Quick glances from side to side told him that. There was the comforting blue of the sky on all sides and below the level of his vision.

As the pair glided smoothly through the air, the peace and satisfaction in Bill's mind were suddenly shattered. They were falling. Falling fast. Much faster than they should. The planned, long arc of descent was being cut short! What was it? What had happened? Then Bill knew. They were caught in a downdraft. Caught in one of the strong, unpredictable winds that surge through the mountains.

The downdraft was forcing them down. Not down to the bottom of the canyon where Bill could again halt his horse an instant before the end. They had jumped too far for that. This time they would hit the sheer canyon wall a full thousand feet above the bottom. A few short feet from their goal and from safety. They would hit the canyon wall head on. There was no place to stop. No place to stand. They would strike the jagged face of the rock with full force and go hurtling down, from pinnacle to rocky pinnacle.

Pecos felt sure nothing could be done to save them. He knew in his heart that hope was gone. But he was a cowpuncher. He had a horse.

And as so many cowpunchers have done in the face of overwhelming odds, he turned to his horse. In a desperate, hopeless instant, he relinquished control. He was no longer the dominating, guiding mind. He was no longer the master. But he did not give up. It was no surrender to fate. He was taking a last chance. *The last chance.*

The Great Pacing White Mustang, with the instinct of his kind, felt the change of authority. He knew at once that his rider had abandoned hope; that now the horse had the last, slim chance of changing failure into success, death into life.

The rocky wall was near. They were falling below the rimrock. Their goal was scarcely a hundred rods away and little more than a rod above them.

And as the horses of many, many, hopeless cowpunchers have done before, and will do again and again, Widow Maker came to the rescue.

The mustang had a problem to solve. A desperate problem. And he solved it. He jumped again. It was a short jump, but it was enough.

8166

Once more he soared up and through the air in a short, graceful arc. The flying pair landed safely on the canyon's rim.

Widow Maker turned and walked back to the canyon. He stretched his neck over the edge of the chasm. He tossed his head and pawed against the rocky surface of the rim. He pointed his muzzle out over the void and whinnied the stallion's cry of victory. The triumphant sound of success filled the conquered space. The Great Pacing White Mustang had won!

Pecos Bill regained his speech. He slapped his horse's withers affectionately. "You done it, pardner," he said. "It took two jumps to do it, but you *done* it!"

A Kind Heart

Now Pecos Bill was not only the biggest cowboy in Texas, the best shot, but he had the kindest heart and the biggest heart, too. He was all heart from the belt up. He liked animals and animals liked him. Widow Maker was the best horse in the world. Norther was the smartest dog, and Souther was a close second.

Other cowpunchers might be content with the best horse and the smartest dog. But not Bill. Not Pecos Bill. He was different. And one way he was different was in his friendship for Henrietta, a hen who was as loyal to Bill as Bill was loyal to her.

Henrietta could usually be found close to the cook shack. Seemed like she was always there, ready to lay an egg if one was needed. No hen could have been more faithful. She would do anything for Pecos Bill. When Bill married Slue Foot Sue, Henrietta got up early in the morning and personally laid the dozen eggs that were necessary for the wedding cake.

And Bean Hole, the cook, never made a mistake when he boiled Henrietta's eggs. If he forgot and let the eggs boil five minutes, when he wanted three minute eggs, it didn't make any difference. All he had to do was to put them back on the stove and boil them two minutes less.

Henrietta's eggs were unusual. So was Henrietta. She never laid a bad egg in her life. Every egg Henrietta delivered was strictly fresh.

Bill always admired her. "Henrietta," he often said, "is the only critter I know who kin work while layin' down. She's workin' when she's layin'. An' she's strictly honest about it, too. That's why I like her. You take a lot of cowpunchers. They are awful liars. An' I cain't stand a liar. When a cowpuncher does a lot of lip work, more likely than not, he's lie'n. But when Henrietta cackles, you kin believe her. She ain't lie'n. She's layin'."

Henrietta was affected by the weather. Perhaps more than most creatures. In the summertime, it got so hot that Bill had to feed her cracked ice to keep her from laying hard-boiled eggs. In Bill's desert country, ice is not often available. As a result, Henrietta laid hard-boiled eggs almost all summer.

And in the winter, he fed her a mixture of gunpowder and match heads. The match heads rubbed against the gritty contents of her gizzard. They caught and burned the gunpowder. Of course, it was damp, and it burned slowly. It heated up her insides enough to keep her eggs from freezing. But it was not entirely successful. It kept the eggs from freezing all right. It also warmed the cockles of her heart, too, and obviously, her cackles. And, unfortunately, it gave her heartburn.

She had an accident one winter. She was caught outdoors when a norther came. It suddenly got cold. It was cold enough to make a polar bear go south. The mercury fell so hard and so fast, it broke a hole in the bottom of the thermometer when it fell. Henrietta pulled one leg up and tucked it in her feathers and kept it warm.

But the other leg, from the bottom of the drumstick down to the ground, didn't have any protection. It froze. The next morning when Bill found her, the leg was as stiff and brittle as an icicle. And like an icicle, it melted away when Bill put her back of the stove to thaw out. A sourdough poultice saved her life. But the leg was gone.

She seemed to have little or no future. Of all creatures, a hen with one leg is truly unfortunate. She had nothing to stand on when she wanted to scratch. Bill's inventive genius came to the rescue. He carved a wooden leg for her out of a cottonwood stick. She got around pretty well with her new peg leg, and had something to stand on when she scratched.

That was all very well. It was interesting enough to see a hen with a wooden leg. But a real surprise came the following summer. Henrietta, hatched a flock of chickens. An even dozen, in keeping with her usual custom. Every one of the chicks took after his mother. Every single one of those chicks had a wooden leg.

The following winter was even colder than the

one when Henrietta lost her leg. It turned cold and it stayed cold. There was no game in the frozen hills. None on the bleak mesas. Henrietta kept on laying eggs but her chicks had to go into the stewpot. Bean Hole wept tears into the gravy, and Pecos Bill pulled up his belt a notch.

Just when Bean Hole was scraping the bottom of the flour barrel, Pecos rescued a small wagon train. Its guide had been killed by Indians and the people were hopelessly lost. Lost and starving. This was no time to bring dozens of hungry people to an empty cook shack. But Pecos Bill had a kind heart. What if it had been a hard winter? Of course game was scarce, "scarce as hen's teeth," but Henrietta couldn't lay enough eggs to feed a wagon train of people.

Pecos Bill threw his saddle on Widow Maker and started off. It was a bitter cold day but somehow he would find food for the stewpot. First, he made his way down into a deep canyon. That, he reasoned, was where the game would go to seek protection from the storm and the cold. He must have meat for those hungry families. He could not fail.

His luck was bad. Even the frozen silences of the canyon failed to give up a wild animal, failed to give the food so desperately needed. As the sun turned toward the horizon, he had just about decided he would have to go back to camp empty-handed. Suddenly, a blacktail deer flashed past on a low hillside about 1200 yards away. It was an easy shot and, as the smoke from his gun disappeared and the echoes rumbled away in the frozen distance, the deer dropped.

Another deer bounded up and away. Bill had a single-shot Sharps rifle. The kind the buffalo hunters used. There was no time to reload. A six-shooter did not have enough range for the long shot the second deer gave him. He could not afford to lose that second deer. At a touch, Widow Maker sprang forward. The mustang could run the deer down. In a few minutes, it was over. Two deer. Meat. The wagon train was saved.

He lost no time in dressing the game. He tied the legs of the deer together, threw them over his palomino, and started on the long, dangerous trip to camp.

His trail led him up along the side of the canyon. As it rose, it became a narrow ledge on the side of the rock wall. There was no room on this scant trail for the deer to hang down the side of the horse. Bill unloosed the tied legs and lifted the frozen carcasses. He clasped them close to him, one under each arm, and held them tightly.

The reins hung on Widow Maker's neck. The mustang would pick his way along the narrow ledge up the ice-covered trail. It was a long chance he was taking. Bill was quite aware of that. But food must reach the starving wagon train as soon as possible. There was no time to take the longer, safer way to camp.

At his right, the cliff soared abruptly upward. At his left, a sheer wall dropped to the valley below. The steep trail curved in and out, following the curves and breaks in the rough, irregular rock.

The sun was sinking rapidly, but it was still daylight. Darkness would soon fall. Shadows from the canyon's rim to the west had spread across the space below, covering the sharp spires of the towering pines with a purple veil. He must hurry.

The path turned a sharp corner at a point where the ledge seemed to hang lightly between heaven and earth. As Widow Maker picked his way along, the curtain of stone opened upon a new vista. Bill's heart skipped a beat. Two beats. Three. Then it pounded hard in a futile effort to regain its lost time, for there before him, crouching squarely in his path, the slender slits of peering eyes flashing like the hot embers of a fire of hate, was a wild cat!

Instinctively, his hand made a movement toward his gun. It was a natural reaction. But he caught himself in time. He could not shoot. Each arm was loaded with a stiff, frozen carcass. To drop one cer-

tainly would result in the loss of desperately needed meat. It probably would throw Widow Maker off balance on the precarious, icy trail, and result in the loss of everything.

It was the first time in his life that a wild cat had given Pecos Bill a moment's concern. He could handle a wild cat with his bare hands. But his hands were busy.

The wild cat crouched low, mad with hunger. It advanced steadily, its evil eyes glaring.

Bill was struggling for an answer to the approaching danger. He must find it, and quickly! Then a new and added danger came into view. The wild cat's mate, a larger and even more ferocious creature, emerged from behind the next bend in the trail.

Pecos knew that hunting had been poor for him. It was also bad for these wild animals. They had been drawn to attack him by the smell of fresh meat and blood. They were killers and he was face to face with them.

His wildly racing brain was searching for an answer. Escape? How to escape? The cliff at his right rose straight up. There was no escape there. At his left was a chasm. A sheer drop to sudden death! His right stirrup rubbed against the wall. His left stirrup hung out over space!

There was only one thing to do. Turn back! But

Widow Maker could never turn on that narrow ledge. There was barely room to stand, to go forward. No. There was no turning.

There might still be a way. Widow Maker had been able to walk forward, up the icy trail. He might be able to back down. He might! The Great Pacing White Mustang saw the danger. He, too, saw the only way of escape. Gingerly, he started to back down the trail.

Bill's leg rubbed against the cold, rough, rock wall as the horse made his way backward down the slender ledge in a desperate hope of somehow finding safety. The path was wider a hundred rods below. Perhaps there, Bill might find a chance to meet his relentless attackers, unburdened and unencumbered.

Pecos turned his head. He was no whiffle bird. He was nothing like a whiffle bird. That bird flies backward because he wants to know where he has been and doesn't care where he is going. But Pecos Bill knew where he had been, and he cared where he was going. He cared very much.

The Great Pacing Mustang also turned his head to glance back. The quick glance had revealed a new truth to Pecos Bill. The same grim truth came to Widow Maker. For there in the path of retreat was a mountain lion!

It was all over. They were lost. They were lost, and the wagon train would starve. The hungry animals approached slowly, relentlessly.

Something would happen soon. Hunger was the force that was driving three wild animals to attack. The attack came. The mountain lion opened his mouth wide and roared. The roar drove the first wild cat to attack. She sprang. Pecos Bill ducked. Widow Maker ducked. The wild cat soared over their heads, her outstretched claws whistling in the wind.

Bill felt the cold air swirl across the back of his neck. The full, free-throated roar of the mountain lion did not fade off in a vicious snarl. It stopped abruptly, as if cut off in the middle. The shrill cry of the wild cat ended sharply at the same time. There was silence.

Once again Pecos turned in the saddle. Two of the enemy were out of the battle. They were out of the battle with Pecos Bill and Widow Maker. But they were in another. A losing battle for both.

The wild cat had overshot her mark. She had sailed over the horseman, right into the mountain lion's open mouth. Her head had plowed into the lion's gullet up to the shoulders. The lion had a mouthful. A mouthful of wild cat. It was more than he could chew. For a few frantic seconds the ledge was burdened with flying claws. The wild cat could not back out, and the mountain lion could not back away.

The only noise was the scratch of claws against stone, and the thud of threshing bodies. The lion's hind leg slipped off the trail. In the struggle, the other hind leg lost its place on the ledge. The two animals, firmly welded together, wavered for a moment on the brink. Then they disappeared. There was silence as the space below devoured them.

But still there was no safety. Another wild cat remained on the trail. Bill turned to face him. The wild cat did not wait. He sprang. Once again the man ducked down and lay close to the mustang's neck. Once again the horse lowered his proud head. And once again a wild cat overshot his mark.

It was a beautiful jump, well calculated to destroy the victim. Gleaming teeth, outstretched claws and a killer's heart. It was a majestic, long jump. That was what was wrong with it. It was too long. Just barely too long. One claw seized on a few hairs from Widow Maker's forelock. Another sliced through the back of the brim of Pecos Bill's twenty-four-gallon Stetson. But that was all.

The wild cat hit the ledge and slid to a halt. Small rocks and pieces of ice, torn loose from the trail, rolled to the edge of the ledge and disappeared into the void below. The wild cat turned as if to resume the attack, but he thought better of it. His mate was lost. He was unnerved. He had had his chance and he had missed. Pecos Bill and Widow Maker were going up the trail. He could pursue them. He could attack from the rear. Instead, he snarled a small, bitter snarl of disgust, turned and started down to the canyon floor below. In spite of hunger, he seemed to be a wild cat with a new determination.

Bill glanced back again as Widow Maker approached another turn in the trail. "That wild cat has got somethin' on his mind," he said to Widow Maker. "I got to remember to come back to this-here canyon, an' find out what it is."

They soon gained the canyon rim. The Pacing White Mustang of the plains was free of the narrow limitations of a treacherous trail, free of marauding beasts. He hit his famous pacing gait and in a short time reached the wagon camp. The precious burden of deer meat soon became grub, and grub restored the life that had been ebbing.

Bill hunted, and fed the camp. He rode to Hell's Gate Gulch and told the boys where he was and what he was doing. Winter passed and spring came. Wagon wheels and harness had been repaired. The wagon train was ready to move on. And Pecos was going to guide them.

The night before the train was to move, Bill was

sitting beside the fire. It was evident he had something on his mind. Gun Smith was in camp that
night. "What's worryin' you, Bill," he said.

"I hate to admit it," Bill replied, "but I jest cain't
seem to git that wild cat out of my mind."

"What wild cat is that?"

"The one that got away on the trail up the canyon.
As he went walkin' down the trail, it jest struck me
real hard that he had somethin' he was goin' to do,"
Bill answered.

"All wild cats act like they are goin' to do somethin'," Gun observed.

"Shore. I know that. But most wild cats has got
somethin' on their mind fer right now. This cat
seemed to have somethin' on his mind fer the future."

"Why don't you go an' see what it was?"

"I cain't do that. The train is ready to move," said
Bill.

"That don't make no difference. Another day's
delay won't hurt none. They bin here all winter,"
Gun said.

"Wal," said Pecos, "if you think it's all right, I
believe I will go back an' see about that cat. I hate
to have a wild cat runnin' around loose that tried to
kill me. So I think I'll jest go back an' kill him. He
ain't up to no good. I know that."

Bill saddled Widow Maker and was gone before

the camp was awake the next morning. At dusk he rode back into camp. In silence, he unsaddled Widow Maker and ate supper.

Gun waited for the big cowpuncher to tell the story. But Bill didn't say anything. He wasn't grimly silent. He wasn't pleasantly silent. He was just silent.

Cowboys aren't given to asking questions. And Gun Smith above all things was a cowpuncher. But he couldn't stand it any longer. Anyway, it wasn't like asking a stranger where he came from, or what his name was. Gun got up, stirred the fire and put another log on. When he sat down, it was beside Pecos Bill.

He waited for a decent moment, hoping that Bill would tell him what happened. But Bill didn't talk. Finally Gun asked, "Did you find that wild cat?"

"Yep," Bill replied after a pause.

"Did you shoot him?" Gun asked softly.

"Nope," said Bill.

Gun exploded. He couldn't help it. Bill had gone hunting for a wild cat. He had seen the critter. But he hadn't killed him.

"Why not?" he exclaimed.

"I jest couldn't do it," Bill answered thoughtfully. "Somehow I jest couldn't bring myself to do it."

"Why not?" Gun insisted.

"I always like to see a person improve himself. If

a feller ain't doin' somethin' right, an' if he knows it an' tries to do better, there ain't a man in the world I'd rather help."

"But what's that got to do with wild cats?" demanded Smith.

"It's the same with wild cats. If they try hard to improve themselves, I jest cain't stop 'em. I got to help 'em."

"Look a-here, Bill, tell me about that wild cat!" Gun said, seriously.

"I went back down in that canyon," Bill said, measuring every word. "I went back down that canyon trail. An' I found the varmint all right. I sneaked up on him. He was carryin' on like no other wild cat I ever seen. At first, I couldn't make out what he was doin'."

"What was he doin'? An' why didn't you shoot him?" Gun demanded in a way that cowpunchers rarely spoke to Pecos Bill.

"I couldn't shoot him," said Bill. "Like I say, I jest couldn't. That pore critter remembered what happened to his mate. An' he remembered how it was he come to miss his dinner that day, just because he jumped too far. An' there he was, jest as busy as he could be. An' he was a practicin' short jumps."

Three Bad Men

You might think that Pecos Bill wouldn't have an enemy in the world. But things didn't work out that way. Just because he was so upright and honorable, there were vicious and disreputable men who sought to do him harm.

Those who were thoughtless and careless faced Bill and made their feelings known. Their end was quick and smoky, and there were never any hard feelings when it was over.

But some of Bill's enemies were not so careless. These, having no wish to meet sudden death, nursed their hate at a safe distance and plotted some way to do harm to Bill, without risking their own skins.

It was well known that Bill set great store by his

pet mountain lion, Scat. Anything that hurt Scat would hurt Bill. So three of the worst villains, with a grudge against Bill, finally cooked up a scheme to kill the big cougar.

Plotting against Scat was a foolish notion, but these scoundrels were foolish men. They should have known the big cat was indestructible. Everyone knows a cat has nine lives. If they had thought about it, they would have realized they would have to kill the cougar nine times.

The truth of the matter probably is, even that would not have been enough. An ordinary house cat has nine lives. No one knows how many lives Bill's big cat had. Pecos had wondered about it. He even started to keep track of the number of times the big cat should have died, but didn't. But he lost count, so no one ever really did know. Curiosity will kill a cat, they say. But even curiosity couldn't kill Scat.

For a long time, the villains concealed their evil plans. Then one day their chance came. They discovered the mountain lion at the far end of Bill's calf pasture. That was in the northwest corner of what is now New Mexico. They were in a draw behind steep wooded hills, hidden from view, where they had been branding some of Pecos Bill's calves. There was little chance of being discovered.

The lion was occupied in one of his favorite pastimes, eating. He had just brought down a big black bear. The tough, stringy meat was a tasty snack for the catamount. The big cat had a generous appetite and considered all things to be victuals until they were proven otherwise.

Bill's enemies came as close as they dared. They drew their hog legs, took careful aim, and fired. The cat swished his tail as if to shoo away some annoying flies. The villains each emptied five more bullets in quick succession into the cat. If they expected the beast to fall, they were mistaken. While he showed signs of vexation, he did not quit his meal. The evil fellows drew their other guns, for they were two-gun men, and each emptied six more bullets into the lion's liver.

Still, the cougar did not quit eating. The guns were loaded again, and fired again. The mountain lion continued to line his flue with bear meat. Once Scat started to eat, he never quit until the food was gone.

The surprised attackers were determined to finish the big beast, so they sat down on a rock and spent the whole morning throwing lead at the catamount. The lion did not fall, but the lead kept pouring into him along with the bear meat. Soon, he got so full of lead and meat that he couldn't stand up. His knees buckled under him. He lay there and closed his eyes,

possibly with the idea of trying to sleep off a dinner that somehow seemed a little heavy for him.

The three bad men seized upon the new opportunity. They approached, and one of them cut at the lion's neck with a bowie knife. The hard steel of the knife broke when it struck the cat's scruff. But an ax did the deed.

Then, to make doubly sure and destroy the evidence of their crime, the butchers dug a deep hole and buried the cat. They covered the grave with rocks.

Sixty yards away, they finished their grisly work and buried the mountain lion's head. They rolled more boulders on the newly-turned earth.

Satisfied with their villainy, the trio mounted their horses and rode away with evil grins of satisfaction. For the moment they felt the false rewards of treachery and cowardice. They drove the calves they had branded and stolen from Pecos Bill before them.

But their evil motives were thwarted, for the next morning the big cat came trotting up the trail to the ranch, carrying his head in his mouth.

Bill was worried for a moment. But Bean Hole, the cook, came to the rescue. He made a poultice of sourdough. After Bill fastened the head and body together, he put the sourdough poultice on the wound. He put the cat on a light diet of beans and sourdough biscuits. Bean Hole always said his sourdough would cure anything. And he was right. The cat got well. But he wasn't very active for several weeks until he got the lead poisoning out of his system.

Bill was kind and generous and thoughtful of others. He disliked violence. But sometimes it seemed necessary to throw a certain amount of lead around. This, clearly was one of those occasions. No one could abuse Bill's cat. While he seldom fired a gun in anger, there was a grim look about him as he strapped on his weapons, mounted Widow Maker and set off. His enemies were well mounted, but Bill gave Widow Maker his head. It was not long until the fugitives came into view. When he saw they were driving his calves away, he gritted his teeth tighter and a hard look fixed upon his jaw.

The sight of the quarry was a challenge to the great golden horse. He hit the ground on the high places. In a short time the distance was closed. The outlaws abandoned the stolen calves and put spurs to their horses. Bill continued to gain on them, and soon they pulled to a stop. The dust of the desert swirled up and drifted lazily away.

During the ride, Bill had time to think about the end of the chase. The grim look disappeared. Now, sadness of a sort was deeply etched on his face.

"Strangers," he said, "I have only good thoughts for you in my heart. I wish you no harm. It's probably jest your hard luck but, unfortunately, you are sittin' right where I'm aimin' to shoot."

He paused a courteous and decent moment to give the lawless fellows a chance to reach for their artillery. The men had no chance. No real chance. But as a drowning man clutches at a straw, the rascals started digging for blue lightning.

Pecos Bill was never one to think evil of a man, and in his heart he found it almost impossible to believe that a gun was drawn in malice. But it happened all the time, to Bill's never-ending surprise.

"It seems to me," he often said, "that people would learn. Why cain't they be kind and gentle? Or at least wise? They ought to know that when a feller starts rollin' his gun, that I got to do somethin' about it. And then, of course, it seems that there is always some windows made in a skull."

The posse that had followed Bill came tearing up after it was all over.

"What happened, Bill?" asked Gun Smith, who was in the lead. He pulled his bronc to a dusty halt, dismounted and walked toward the three lifeless figures sprawled on the rocky earth.

Three-fingered Ike pulled his mustang up short. He looked down with a quick, skilled eye. "Looks to me like they got their horns sawed off, close and quick," he said.

The other cowpunchers drew close. "This hombre had his gun drawed," Gun Smith observed.

Every man in the posse nodded in agreement. Gun shook his head sagely. "It looks like a clear case of self-defense to me," he concluded.

"Yep," Three-fingered Ike agreed. "A corpse and cartridge occasion. Unfortunate, but necessary."

Alkali Ike edged his bronco through the posse. "They was rustling calves," he said. "I ain't familiar with the penalty fer tryin' to kill a mountain lion. But them hombres has paid their lawful an' proper debt to society fer rustlin' calves."

Battle with the Sockdolager

AFTER Pecos Bill convinced the three bad men that it was foolish to meddle with Scat, there was law and order in Texas. Sometimes, a stranger would come along and criticize Bill, suggesting that he had a quarrelsome disposition. This was far from the truth.

Bill was a peaceable man. If he occasionally went out of his way to look for a fight, he had a good reason. Once, he wore out two sets of Widow Maker's shoes, trying to find a bad man who might have been overlooked. Most of the time he was a real friendly fellow, but if anyone picked a fight with Pecos Bill, there was no backing out. It was a fight to the finish.

One of the biggest fights Pecos Bill ever had developed on a trip he took just before roundup time.

Whenever he had a few days to spare, he liked to ride over the Pacific and take a look at the ocean. The history books say that the Pacific Ocean was discovered by Balboa on September 25, 1513. The geography books say the same thing. But the truth is that nobody paid much attention to the Pacific until Pecos started riding over there for a holiday once in a while.

Bill was a strong, active, restless person and he saw his own kind in the powerful Pacific. He was a man of the wide, open spaces. Space was necessary for him, and he recognized the ocean for what it was, and he liked it.

On his trips to the Pacific coast, Widow Maker, the Great Pacing White Mustang, was Bill's constant companion. Scat, his mountain lion, and Rat, his rattlesnake, usually accompanied him. There was something in Pecos Bill that seemed to urge him westward. His paw and maw had been the same way. Westward. Westward. Always westward.

The Pacific Ocean seemed about as far as a man could go. At least, as far as he really wanted to go. Bill was a cowpuncher. He was not a sailor. He took long swims in the ocean. Widow Maker, Scat and Rat joined him. A happy, carefree party.

It would seem that such an innocent, friendly activity on a wide, empty ocean would disturb no one. But not so. There lived in the Pacific a school of monsters. The original denizens of the deep! Larger than whales. They had the ferocity of the tiger shark. The savagery of the giant ray. The wiliness of the great octopus. And the nasty disposition of the barracuda.

The denizens of the deep were bossed by the biggest of the lot, a giant, dirty-gray monster that ruled them with an iron fin. This boss of them all was known as the Sockdolager of the Sea. He was bad-tempered beyond description. The only joy he had in life was being disagreeable. And he searched the ocean to fight and prey upon other giants of the sea. When he found them, the wild flapping of tails, the thrashing of great fins lashing the water, the frenzied leaps into the air brought death and destruction to smaller creatures. Sometimes, the titanic splashes swelled into storms that ravaged the coasts of four continents.

One day Pecos and his horse, with Rat and Scat, were swimming in the ocean. They had just crossed Death Valley and they were hot and tired. The cool water refreshed them. They were having a wonderful time.

The Sockdolager of the Sea could not abide the joy of Pecos Bill and his small, friendly party. He looked upon the cowpuncher as an enemy. An enemy

to be destroyed. He lurked around in the dim, blue-green distances, taking the measure of the man. The Sockdolager had been the boss of all the giant denizens for so long that he thought he owned the ocean. When he was satisfied that he was bigger and stronger than Pecos Bill, he churned his broad tail from side to side and shot toward his victim.

Bill was in deep water when he saw the fleshy monster coming. His first thought was of danger. Natural for a cowpuncher in a land where death was the penalty if danger was not recognized at first sight.

But Pecos had a friendly spirit. He could not help

hoping he had found a new friend. The creature approached rapidly. "He swims real good," Pecos thought. "If he wants to race, he'll probably beat me." That would have been a new experience for Bill. But there was no envy, no jealousy. Just a fact to be faced.

Then the truth came to Pecos in a flash. This was no friend. The thought had no sooner formed in his mind, when the enormous jaws approaching him opened. He saw row after row of sharp, evil teeth standing like stained, closely-packed gravestones on Boot Hill.

Pecos Bill had been through many dangerous ad-

ventures. If this was not death staring him in the face, it looked like it. On foot, on land, he would side step. On horseback, he would rein sharply away. But in the sea, in a strange element, quite different from his familiar ground, what could he do? There was no time to think. His right arm shot out. His left followed. The ocean pressed against his hands as he drew them back in a rapid motion. He shot through the water. The jaws of death snapped shut with a crash!

Water submerged him as the waves set in motion by the malignant mouth washed past. But Bill was safe. The vicious teeth had missed him. Missed him by the thickness of a frog hair.

The huge body was surging past. The best defense was offense. But what could he do while he was in the water? With scarcely a second thought, he kicked. His big toe hit the hard, scaly hide. He winced. "Jest like the time I kicked a razorback hog when I was barefoot," he thought, as the memory of an old, childhood lesson brought a smile to his lips.

But he would get his licks in anyway. The long creature was still sliding past him. Treading water, Bill raised his shoulders above the surface. Crash! A quick right. Bang! A left to the monster's ribs. The scales cracked where his fist struck. Blood dripped down over the wet, stony surface. He saw it melt away in the white-flecked waves of the ocean.

Scat and Rat swam to Bill's side ready to aid him. He waved them away and they obediently made for shore.

He heard a choking sound as the monster gasped with pain. Still treading water, he regained his balance. He looked forward toward the creature's head. The big jaws were opening again. Widow Maker! He was making for Widow Maker!

The horse was closer to the shore. He was in the water up to the hamstrings. Could Widow Maker survive? For a terrible moment Pecos held his breath. But Widow Maker had seen Bill's miraculous escape. He, too, jumped aside. To the other side. The Sockdolager was outwitted. He missed. Missed by the thickness of the root of a rock! But missed!

Widow Maker was standing on the ocean bottom, so he had a footing of sorts. He waited as the enemy stretched past. At the proper time, when he was ready, he shot out a kick that shattered the big fish's scales over an area the size of a horse blanket!

Bill grinned. "That hoss sure gave him a skinful of ache," he said.

The Sockdolager turned with a grunt and a groan, and sought safety in the depths of the ocean. A few strong strokes brought Pecos Bill to shore. He and the big palomino walked through the restless surf to dry land. Scat and Rat were there to meet them.

Bill turned and gazed out over the water. The

Sockdolager of the Sea was gone! "Bet he feels like he's got a gizzard full of gravel," he said, as he combed his fingers through the palomino's silver mane.

"That seagoin' critter was spittin' kind of thick," he said. "If he comes around again, I'll cool him off with a little hot lead." He pulled the cinches tight and started off for his Hell's Gate Gulch Ranch.

The days that passed were busy ones. It was time for the roundup. And after that there was the long drive north to the Montana ranges. To tell the truth, Bill quite forgot about his fight with the Sockdolager of the Sea. But the seagoing titan did not forget. He had hated the big cowpuncher from the beginning. As he lurked in the safe depths of the ocean, he nursed his wounds and his rage. The wounds healed but the rage grew. He would have revenge.

When work slackened, Bill saddled the palomino, called Scat and Rat, and set off for the Pacific. He dismounted on a rise overlooking the ocean. He was at ease and at peace with the world. He slapped Widow Maker's golden neck and idly ran his hand down over the horse's withers and across his broad back. The wide, peaceful expanse of the Pacific spread out before him.

Widow Maker could smell danger twenty miles away. Suddenly he thrust his sharp, pointed ears for-

ward. He nickered a soft warning. Danger was near.
Bill saw and heard. But where was the danger in this
peaceful scene?

The answer came! The Sockdolager's back rose
above the water. A rock the size of a house was
cupped in his tail. There was a muscular flourish.
A flash! The boulder sped through the air like a
meteor, straight for the unguarded man and horse.

Bill hit the leather as fast as a scared fly jumping
away from a fly swatter. But he was not jumping
away from his attacker. He was racing toward him.
The pacing mustang answered his touch and sped
down the hill. Neither man nor horse would dodge
again! "The last time we seen that critter," Bill mut-
tered, "we was in the water. We didn't have no more
chance than a bobtailed cow in fly time."

He heard the measured sound of the galloping
hoofs beneath him. "Wrasslin' that varmint in the
water would be jest about as safe as tryin' to brand
a mule's tail without no hobbles," he said.

The rock soared over their heads and landed with
a crash on the rise where they had been only a few
seconds before. A quick glance over his shoulder
gave him the sight of Scat bounding along down the
slope. The mountain lion was sending forth his fierce
cry of battle at every jump. Rat was curled around
the catamount's neck and was rattling his defiance

at the world in general and the Sockdolager in particular.

"Thanks fer the warnin'," Pecos said to the mustang. "If you hadn't nickered when you did, we might of got splattered around all over the top of that hill. If I'd lived through that, I'd of bin smacked down so low I'd have to climb up a ladder to milk a snake."

The Sockdolager was swimming southward. He turned to see the effect of his well-planned blow. But instead of seeing Pecos Bill and Widow Maker crushed by the boulder, he saw them charging toward him. At the same time, Bill reached for his hardware. Bang! Bang! Bang! Bang! Twelve sharp reports echoed from the mountains to the sea as the guns went off.

Pecos saw the heavy lead slugs spatter against the monster's scales. He should have known. He had kicked the creature and had hurt his own toe. It should have been clear. The 45's wouldn't do.

Still riding at breakneck speed, he emptied his Winchester into the monster's left gill. Just a show of blood. No damage. None.

Bill's finger's closed on his lariat on the saddle horn. It was the same lariat he had made years before out of the hides of the toughest old mossback steers in Texas. And nothing can be tougher. Not even the Sockdolager of the Sea, the boss of the terrible denizens of the deep!

As the hoofs thundered on, he built a loop. "The last time we met up with that ocean-lopin' varmint, it weren't no fair fight. But this time, ole feller, I got my equipment. We'll fight him down to a shadow, won't we?"

Widow Maker heard. He agreed. He was game for the fight. The steady, unbroken rhythm of sharp-shod hoofs gave his response.

The loop opened wide in the air. The leather noose grew larger as Bill whirled it around his head. Suddenly he released it. The rawhide circle shot out above the water with a whine and a swish as it tore through the air. It fell over the head of the mighty Sockdolager of the Sea. The braided leather slipped through the honda, and closed tight back of the gills and in front of the pectoral fins. Over the withers, so to speak.

When the rope tightened, Widow Maker went into a "set" as a good cow pony should. The rope pulled tight along the first dorsal fin on the Sockdolager's back.

On the range, the critter would now spill off its feet. On the range, Bill would now swing from the saddle and hog-tie his legs while Widow Maker held the rope tight.

But what to do with a Sockdolager of the Sea in the sea? There were no feet to tie. The Sockdolager was not on its back. What to do? The answer was clear. There was only one thing to do. Fight it out!

The Sockdolager met the tightened lariat with a surge of his broad tail. Widow Maker bounced forward with the pull. His hoofs sank again in the rocky surface of the earth. The horse stepped in the water that had splashed up from the sea. His feet slipped and his right rump hit the ground. The earth shuddered. A flurry of feet beat a tattoo against the earth's surface. Around the flat depression left by his rump, irregular ridges were piled high.

A great geographical fact had been accomplished. A fact that would take an important part in the fight only just beginning.

As the great tail moved in massive arcs through the water, whirlpools formed, sucking sharks and devil fish down into the black, unknown depths of the ocean floor. Waterspouts swirled up, pulled albatross and gull into their dark gullets, and drenched the friendly white clouds. The clouds melted away in the storm of water. The fortunate ones, further away, scurried to safety.

The Sockdolager writhed and turned, jumped and jerked. He pitched and plunged. A cataract of ocean billowed up and out. A cataclysm engulfed the horse and rider. The torrent rose and fell as the great sea monster fought on!

The Great Pacing Mustang's hoofs were firmly planted once again. But the Sockdolager was making headway. He was pulling man and horse. But the horse was not giving ground, except when the pull was so great he was lifted forward in prodigious, involuntary jumps. He cut out gorges and canyons where the hoofs sliced into the earth. He piled up mountain ranges where the rocks were thrust aside.

When his feet were solidly fixed, when he held firm, Bill could see that the monster was pulling them southward. The dally welta was holding fast. There was no slipping of the hitch at the saddle horn. The tough rawhide lariat was not stretching even though it was wet. It was pulled tighter than a worm with a robin on one end.

Through the welter of confusion and scramble, Bill saw that the Sockdolager was winning. They were being drawn southward. How? Why?

Then he understood. The land itself was stretching. Stretching out to sea. With the Sockdolager on one end of Pecos Bill's famous lasso, with Widow Maker on the other end, something had to give! The Sockdolager didn't. The rope couldn't. And Widow Maker wouldn't!

It was the land that was giving. Southern California and Northwestern Mexico. The firm, hard, solid land was yielding. It was being pulled out into a rough, sharp point, stabbing southward along the coast of Mexico!

Back and forth the scramble went. First the Mustang would prevail. In a confusion of hammering hoofs, he would draw the sea monster back. Then, the Sockdolager, with a burst of strength, would surge southward. The Mustang maintained his stance. And the land stretched again. And on and on. Forward and back. But in the end, slowly to the south.

Pecos, sharing the fight, found time to wonder how far the land would stretch. Would California and Mexico hold together? Or would they tear apart at the boundary? If the boundary line split, if the land gave out, if it broke off, the battle was lost. He knew that.

The fight went on. The land stretched. The boundary line held. Two hundred, four hundred, seven hundred miles!

He loaded his Winchesters repeatedly and emptied them into the Sockdolager. Into the gills. Into the narrow spaces between the giant fish's scales. It was small help. But some. The loss of each small, trickling barrel, gallon, or even a single drop of blood weakened the enemy. But it was Widow Maker's fight. Yes. It was the fight of the Great Pacing White Mustang of the Plains!

The strength of the land was almost gone. Horse and man were near exhaustion. The Sockdolager was fighting strong. It seemed to be a losing fight for the Mustang. Then the tugs on the lariat suddenly became weaker. Widow Maker took full advantage of the new weakness. He scrambled back northward, pulling the Sockdolager behind. The monster's lower lip was dragging. His sharp teeth gouged down into the confusion of water, rocks and soil. The bony fins, hard as steel, plowed through the distressed and torn earth's surface.

A great wash of ocean piled up ahead of the helpless, but still fighting, monster of the deep. The end of a great historical and geographical fact was at hand.

The stretched-out, southward-pointing land is now known as Lower California. Its rough and rugged surface remains mute testimony of Widow Maker's contest with the Sockdolager of the Sea. The dry, barren surface, scarred and torn by dry arroyos and canyons still shows how hard it was stretched and squeezed. It is the literal truth. The juice was all squeezed out of it.

As the Sockdolager was pulled along, the Gulf of California was made. Dug out by the teeth and the fins of the Sockdolager.

Pecos Bill rode north up the Colorado River, dragging the Sockdolager behind him. The bulk of the inert creature pushed the ocean water ahead. Like a great, moving dam, the torrent backed up. Far up the Colorado River. It reached its banks and spilled out into the depression Widow Maker had made early in the fight when he slipped and fell on his rump.

A great inland sea was formed. Bill pulled the Sockdolager into the new-made sea. He was a weakened, conquered hulk. Near death.

The Colorado River, relieved of its burden, emptied the ocean water that had flooded its banks back into the Gulf of California. The sudden release of the pent-up flood washed out the Grand Canyon of Arizona. Made it deeper and wider. Traces of Sockdolager blood remain and still color the rocks of the Grand Canyon.

The new sea remained. Hemmed in by the mountains Widow Maker kicked into being when the fight first started.

There are always those who scoff at truth. But there is a power in books. Books can supply the facts, within limits. And it can be proven from books that a great sea once covered the Imperial Valley of California. For when Widow Maker slipped and fell, he leveled out the place now known as the Imperial Valley.

Some things are simply and easily done. "With a twist of the wrist," they sometimes say. It is true. Widow Maker made Imperial Valley with a bump of the rump. The Salton Sea, now little more than a shallow lake, is all that remains of Widow Maker's great sea. The true student of Pecos Bill will not question the facts.

But there is further proof. It is circumstantial evidence, it is true. It involves a modicum of conjecture. But it is convincing.

Bill did not kill the helpless, defenseless Sockdolager. Cats like fish, as everyone knows. It is easy to imagine that Scat, Bill's big cat, killed the Sockdolager. In fact, it is almost necessary to believe it. He could not eat it all. So, in the course of time, the big fish returned to the soil.

Everyone knows fish make good fertilizer. The Indians, for example, placed a fish in each hill of corn at planting time. In Imperial Valley, the soil is fertile. No fish except the Sockdolager would be big enough to fertilize it all. Therefore, it must have been the Sockdolager. The same Sockdolager that was fought to a standstill and dragged there by Pecos Bill and Widow Maker.

Too Hot to Handle

No ONE knows what Southern California looked like before the famous battle with the Sockdolager. No reliable records are available.

It is clear, however, that Southern California has changed greatly since that famous battle. The great inland sea is no longer to be seen, for example. No more than traces of its former existence remain. Dim and subtle traces, clear for the most part only to the scientific mind.

The mountain ranges which Widow Maker's sharp hoofs pounded and cut into existence remain as visible and lasting evidence of the titanic struggle. But even they have been affected by the passage of time.

Southern California has furnished adventure and excitement for all the years from the early settlers to the present day. But nothing like it did in the days of Pecos Bill. In a land that gets pulled out of shape by a Sockdolager, or anything else for that matter, strange, unlikely things may happen.

Such a land, having been pulled and twisted and stretched is obviously likely to have all the water wrung out of it. Deserts are the result. And of course, there are deserts in Southern California. Newly-made mountains and an inland sea are readily apparent and understandable. They can be seen and recognized for what they are. But the subtle, obscure and mysterious effects wrought upon such a tortured land are not so easily understood.

Pecos Bill had long had a ranch over on the coast. Some time had elapsed since his battle with the Sockdolager and it was once again time to make an inspection trip. He tossed his saddle on Widow Maker and started off in company with Three-fingered Ike. It was an uneventful trip until he reached the area that had borne the full burden of the battle with the Sockdolager.

He was surprised and interested to see that the sea he and his palomino had created was still there. "Wal, dang my hide," he said to Three-fingered Ike as they reached the summit of a mountain that com-

manded the valley, "that sea is still there. I kinda thought it would roll back into the ocean where it belongs."

"How did all that water git there?" asked Ike. "It wasn't there the last time I was over this way."

"Oh, Widow Maker an' me had a little difference of opinion with a Sockdolager some time back. An' that come about in the tussle," Bill replied casually.

True to character, Bill had never said anything about the battle. And even now, he referred to "a" Sockdolager, instead of "the" Sockdolager. His modesty was always with him. He never talked about himself. If he went around telling people he had conquered the Sockdolager of the Sea, some folks might have got the idea that he was boasting. It was not Bill's nature to boast. So he said nothing. Fortunately, there were several reliable witnesses and as a consequence the complete story is known.

Ike knew it would be useless to ask for details. Anyway, Ike was a man who did not ask questions. Instead, he merely squinted across the broad expanse of water and to the new mountains beyond.

"Things in general looks different," he said.

"Yep. I guess so," said Bill as he slid from the saddle. "The real estate was purty well chawed up around here."

It was dusk. The sun had fallen below the jagged ridge to the west. In a short time it would be dark.

Ike dismounted and the two men strolled toward a swift mountain stream. It was a stream with a rough, steep course down the rocky side of a mountain that had been thrown up in the memorable battle. The horses followed slowly, stopping to nibble at the grass that grew thick and green on the banks of the small gulch that led to the river.

"What's the matter with the hosses, I wonder?" asked Bill, half to himself.

"Why?" Ike inquired.

"They don't seem to smell that river. That ain't natural. We bin ridin' hard, an' them hosses has every right to be thirsty. They ought to have their ears pointed toward it. By rights, they ought to be nickerin' an' actin' anxious to git down there fer a drink."

"That's right," Ike replied. "A critter kin smell water fer a long ways. Wonder what's the matter with 'em?"

"Don't think it's anything wrong with the hosses," Pecos said. "Must be somethin' the matter with the water. No. Maybe not. Widow Maker knows it's there."

Widow Maker lifted his beautiful head. His nostrils quivered as they received the odor of fresh water. His sharp ears pointed forward. His step quickened as he pressed on ahead of Bill.

Ike's horse, a buckskin mare with two white stockings, still lingered behind, intent on an extra mouthful of the cool, moist refreshing grass. She was unaware that a river was near and lifted her head with surprise when Widow Maker's eager nicker gave her the news. She pulled the reins in Ike's hand tight as she stepped smartly ahead.

These strange events were not lost on Pecos Bill and he resolved to sample the water before he permitted the horses to drink. It was a fast mountain stream. In fact, it was the fastest running water Pecos Bill had ever seen.

He cautioned Widow Maker not to drink. Then he knelt and pressed his lips to the water. He drew back sharply.

Ike saw his puzzled look. "What's the matter?" he asked.

Bill licked his lips cautiously. Then he stooped to drink again. Once more, he jerked his mouth away from the stream. Again, licking his lips, he tasted the water.

"What is it, Bill?"

"Don't quite know exactly," Pecos answered. "Never run into anything like it before."

"It ain't alkali, I wouldn't think. 'Way up here in the mountains," Ike ventured.

"No. It ain't alkali or gyp."

"What is it then, do you suppose?"

Bill put his hand in the water. Quickly, he pulled it out. Then he cupped his hand down in the water and tasted it again.

"It's mighty strange, Ike. I never seen a thing like this before."

"What?"

"They ain't nothin' the matter with the water, 'cept it's flowin' awful fast. It's flowin' so fast the friction almost burns when you touch it. That's prob'ly the reason the hosses didn't smell it. It flows past at such a quick rate that no odor comes off of it."

"It's all right fer the hosses then, ain't it?" Ike asked.

"Shore," Bill replied.

The men loosened the cinches. Widow Maker and the little buckskin mare thrust their noses in the stream. The buckskin jerked her head up. But her thirst was great, so she returned her muzzle to the water.

The horses drank eagerly. The buckskin shook her head and wrinkled her nose repeatedly. Widow Maker began to show similar signs of distress. Bill determined to find the cause.

He examined Widow Maker's nose. "Wal, I declare!" he exclaimed, after careful scrutiny.

"What do you make of it?" Ike asked as he peered at the golden horse's nose.

"We got to watch that water. It's goin' so fast the friction has wore all the hair off the cayuse's nose. Hey! What's the matter with your buckskin?"

The little mare was showing signs of real distress. Bill strode rapidly to the bronco. He took the horse's head in his hands and bent down for close inspection. "This-here might be serious," he gravely announced.

"I should say so," Ike agreed.

"Your buckskin ain't as tough as Widow Maker," said Bill, pointing to the unhappy animal's muzzle. "The friction from that water not only wore her whiskers off, but it wore blisters on the pore critter's nose."

"Blisters?" asked Ike, peering intently, and with an inflection that could not conceal his surprise. Surprise that was about to bloom into disbelief.

"Yep. Blisters! Real, one-hunnert percent blisters! In the circumstances, water blisters is exactly what they ought to be."

Here may have been the discovery, the invention, of water blisters. But the evidence is not clear. Bill never referred to the matter again. So, with the fairness that characterizes biographers of Pecos Bill, no serious claims are made. The point is considered open, and subject to further investigation.

"We got to stop here fer a day or so fer your hoss's nose to git well," Pecos said.

"But we ain't got enough grub," Three-fingered Ike protested. "An' we ain't got no water. None that a body kin drink anyways."

"Lack of grub ain't no problem. Not when you got a gun. Or even if you ain't got a gun, as far as that's concerned. We kin kill some game," Pecos replied. "An' as fer water, we kin make a little pool at the edge of the river. The water will run in an' kinda slow down. At least it will slow down enough so it won't cause no damage. We kin all drink it then."

So it was settled and they made camp. Bill caught and killed a young deer and a yearling bear and put them on the fire to cook. Ike, with the aid of some rocks, made a pool at the river's edge which soon filled with water that was running slowly enough for man and beast to drink.

Before the men began their own meal, Bill rendered some bear grease and doctored the buckskin's sore nose.

"Bear grease will cure everything. Cuts, corns, bruises and rheumatism," he said. "It's good medicine. It practically makes lumbago a pleasure. I guess it will cure blisters, too."

The Hungry Trout

THE NEXT morning Pecos Bill got up early. Ike was sleeping soundly. The big cowpuncher looked at him and resolved to let him sleep. They had been riding hard for three days and the man was tired.

"I ought to remember to take it easy when one of the men is with me," Bill thought. "What's an easy ride fer me an' Widow Maker, is real hard goin' fer others." He wandered off to look at the swiftly moving mountain stream.

The beautiful river, dashing down the mountain, swirling past the rocks and cascading over boulders, brought a pleasant thought. Fish. The river would be full of fine mountain trout. He could see them in the water near the shore, and everywhere they were splashing and jumping at flies.

Trout for breakfast! It was a happy thought. It would not be right to ask the buckskin to travel with a nose swollen big with water blisters. She was no match for Widow Maker. She had been traveling too hard. She was tired. Like Ike, she needed a rest.

Bill looked around for a space of earth free of rocks. He saw a clump of pines some distance from the stream. That would be a good place to find some worms. He took hold of a tree about the size of a man's wrist and pulled it out of the ground. Stooping, he pushed away the small, moist rocks and the earth and started to pick up the worms he needed for bait. As he did so, he was conscious of a strange sound. But he was so intent in catching the worms that he did not look up at once. The worms were big and fat. But they were remarkably agile and seemed unusually eager to escape.

He moved quickly, quickly enough to capture half a dozen worms. The strange sound was growing louder. Too loud now and too close to be ignored. He started to look up and as he did so he was struck a dozen wet blows. All about him. Everywhere. Scarcely knowing what to think, he lifted his head and began to rise from his kneeling position.

The blows were very rapid, repeated, staccato. Not loud. It was like the clapping of hands, many hands. Like the distant, dead barking of a sprightly gun fight. Not as loud as a gun fired from one's own hand. About as loud as the thud of a falling body. But many, many such thuds. What was happening?

A fine mist of water clouded Bill's vision for a brief moment. The blows were hard. But not too hard. Not hard as a rock. More like being slapped with a fish. That was it! Like a fish. As he rose, the simple truth came to him as he wiped the water from his eyes.

That *was* it! He was being slapped by a fish. By many fish. They flapped and flopped down in the crater left where he had pulled up the pine tree. Snapping and threshing about, they fought for the exposed worms. They dug and rooted into the ground for the rapidly retreating worms, like hungry hens in a newly-plowed garden.

Still clutching the bait he had dug, Bill stepped aside to watch the strange sight. It would soon be over for those voracious fish would have the hole picked clean in an instant.

"I'm glad I'm out of that," he thought.

No sooner had the thought formed in his mind than his attention was drawn to a big trout. The fish was down in the hole in the thick of the fight. It paused for an instant.

"That one knows the vittles is all gone," Bill thought. "He'll probably go flappin' back home now."

The big fish gave a flip of his tail. But instead of

going toward the river, he went the other direction. And he had a purpose, for he sprang at Bill's hand! The hand that still held the newly-dug bait. His aim was true, for he snapped the head off a fishworm.

Poor worm! Like any normal worm, it had tried to escape. And it had met with some success. By dint of great exertions, by stretching and contracting, by expanding and shrinking, it had been able to push its head and shoulders through a small opening between the fingers of Bill's carefully but loosely closed fist.

Escape seemed possible for a moment. But no. Not now. Not with such a trout after it.

The worm saw the danger. It knew what to expect though Pecos Bill did not. It tried hard to pull in its neck. The soft, wet skin was forced into tightly-packed wrinkles as it tried to draw its head back to safety. Then the head was gone. Gone with a patch of skin from Pecos' knuckle. Shaved off by the sharp teeth of a hungry trout.

At that instant, the other trout sensed the fish-worm bonanza in Bill's hand. They sprang for the bait, jumping and flapping their tails against the big cowpuncher's legs, hands and body. They jumped so eagerly and so wildly that even his face was flailed by a flood of fins and tails.

Pecos Bill had been in many battles. In a long and active life, he had been at the center of innumerable fights. Most attackers had tried to take his life. Some, his money, his cattle, his horses. But this was the first time anyone or anything had sought to take half a dozen fishworms away from him. He retreated, partly from surprise and partly because he became filled with an uncontrollable mirth.

"Git away thar, you," he shouted as he tried to push the finny onslaught away. At each motion of his hand, a trout would spring, never for a moment forgetting the succulent tidbit in Bill's hand.

His retreat continued toward camp, the fish pursuing him. They twisted between his legs, bouncing up from the ground and flapping against him as they tried repeatedly to reach their goal.

Bill, pursued by the hungry trout, moved backward. Several times he stumbled, but caught himself and was able to keep a precarious balance. But he had no such luck when his heels met the reclining form of Three-fingered Ike. He pitched over backwards and came to rest on the ground.

Three-fingered Ike's eyes opened. He saw Pecos lying on the ground near by. "I jest had a funny dream," he said.

Pecos did not answer. Ike continued, filled with the wonder of his dream. "It was about fish," he said thoughtfully, searching for clear recollection. "Seems like there was a lot of fish dancin' around me an' jest as I was goin'. . ."

The story of his dream was shattered by reality. The cold, wet reality of a fishtail across his face. Then another. And in an instant a tribe of finny creatures was dancing over him, still bent on reaching Pecos Bill.

"What the . . ." Ike exploded as his hands fanned the air and he scrambled out of his soogans, fumbling for his gun.

Pecos was now overcome with a new fit of laughter as he saw Ike's surprise and wonder and mad scrambling. His roars of glee filled the rocky canyon, and the trees bent and swayed.

The frantic fish would be on him in a moment. Lying on his back, he lifted his arm in a long, sweeping motion. His hand opened and the fishworms, the loose gravel and soil that accompanied them, sped through space toward the river. Fish may not know how desirable it is to keep the eye on the ball. But the trout knew all the rules about keeping their fishy eyes on the worms. Not one missed the sight of breakfast flying through the air. As one fish, they flipped about and headed for their quarry like foxhounds after a fleeing fox.

The biggest fish, or the luckiest, or the fastest, caught the worms on the first bounce. Without pause, with only a few flips and flaps, they went on to the river and splashed into its depths.

Poor Three-fingered Ike was scarcely able to understand the sudden attack and retreat. But Bill explained the strange conduct of the hungry fish.

"Wal," Ike exclaimed, "I wouldn't have believed it if I didn't see it myself."

"It all happened jest because I thought some fresh trout fer breakfast would be good," said Bill.

"They would be good, too," Ike agreed. "But I'd rather have 'em on the inside of me, than flappin' all over me on the outside an' wakin' me out of a sound sleep."

"I still aim to have some trout fer breakfast," Bill insisted.

"But how you goin' to ketch 'em? They won't even let you handle the bait," Ike asked.

"Mebby I kin shoot one or lasso one," Pecos said.

"Could try anyway," Ike said doubtfully.

Bill picked up his lariat and, as he walked toward the stream, he built a small loop. The trout were jumping out of the water here and there, lunging at flies, and getting their breakfast in a more conventional trout-like way.

"Better shoot 'em. They're jumpin' fast an' you don't never know where one is goin' to rise," Ike said. "I don't think you . . ."

His words of discouragement were answered by the hiss of Bill's rope as it sang through the air. Ike had never seen a rope travel so fast. It sped over the water faster than a mule's hind foot. The small noose snapped shut on a fine, big trout just as he reached the peak of his quick, graceful arc above the water. The noose tightened back of the gills. The rope stretched tight as the big fish finished his leap with an extra flip of his tail.

The trout dived. Deep. Down. Down. Bill's eyes danced with pleasure. This was going to be a good fight.

But anticipation soon changed to surprise. The rope was tight but there was no fight. No singing line. No quick lunges. No desperate thrusts.

What had happened? Just a steady, tight rope. Nothing more. Ike stepped down toward the bank of the stream. It was morning. The sun was shining brightly behind him and his shadow fell before him as he walked. He almost reached the river when suddenly he threw his hands in the air and let out a sharp, involuntary cry of anguish.

Bill turned quickly. "What's wrong?" he asked.

Ike did not answer. He seemed to be struggling with strong, unseen hands, twisting and turning like a maverick on the end of a tight rope.

"What is it, Ike? What is it?" Bill shouted.

The answer was a strange, incoherent cry. A breathless cry of rage, exertion, despair. Ike wavered and struggled and lunged crazily toward the water.

He seemed to catch himself. He straightened and appeared for a moment to regain his balance. His arms moved wildly. But he was moving toward the river as if drawn by invisible muscles of steel.

Bill hitched his rope around a small boulder with a flick of the wrist and sprang toward his partner. He seized the unfortunate, terrified man by the shoulders and straightened him up.

Then Pecos Bill felt a terrific, unknown power, pulling at him. Grasping Ike tightly, he pulled himself and his companion away. Away from the stream that seemed to be the source of the unknown strength. As he moved back, suddenly the power released its hold. He was free!

Ike sank to the ground, exhausted. After a few deep, relieved gasps he raised his head. "What was it, Bill," he asked.

"Don't rightly know," Pecos replied. "But I shore aim to find out."

Pecos made a few tentative steps toward the water. Then back. Then forward again. He looked up the stream and down. His quick, gray eyes missed nothing. A tentative step again. Then a bold one.

At length, he paused. "Seems like a person kin always run into somethin' new," he said.

"I know I never felt nothin' like that before," said Ike. "It seemed like somethin' strong was pullin' me. Pullin' my head. Pullin' my hair even. Then pullin' my shoulders. But pullin' all over me at the same time, too. I couldn't do nothin'. I felt as weak as an egg dropped on a rock."

"No wonder," said Bill.

"What was it?"

"It was the river, that's all."

"The river?"

"Yep. Look there. Look up an' down that river. What do you notice?" Bill asked.

"Nothin'. Nothin', 'cept . . ."

" 'Cept what?" Pecos insisted.

" 'Cept they ain't no trees on either side of the water. Jest little trees near the stream. Then they grows taller an' taller, gradual-like. They jest kinda slopes up in size. Then there is a row of big trees 'way back. It's the same on each side of the river. Exactly the same."

"That gives you the answer," said Bill.

"It don't give me no answer. What's that got to do with it?"

"Ike, that river is runnin' so fast, it jest carries everything right along with it. Everything. Even shadders. When a shadder hits that river, the river is goin' so fast it jest naturally carries the shadder right along with it, too. If somethin' is attached to the shadder, as is usually the case, course, that somethin' goes right along, too."

"The sun was shinin' behind you," Pecos continued. "Your shadder was stretched out in front. When your shadder hit the water, the pullin' began. An' that's when you felt like you was a gonner."

Ike arose and looked down at the shadow that had come so near to causing his destruction. "But what's that got to do with trees?" he asked.

"Why, it's the same with the trees. When they grow big enough to cast a shadder into that water, the current takes hold an' carries shadder, tree an' all right along with it. If it wasn't fer that ridge on the west, an' that mountain risin' on the east, there wouldn't be a tree in this-here valley."

Ike was not a cowardly man but he stepped respectfully away from the unusual river.

"We got to be kinda keerful about a river that's flowin' as fast as that," said Bill, as he moved back to his neglected fishline.

Several minutes had passed. The rope was still tight. But there was no movement, no action, and in trout fishing, action is expected. Bill pulled on the rope. There was the same, steady resistance. No fight. No tugging. No pulling.

"There ain't no fight in him," said Bill, as he rapidly pulled the rope in. "It's jest a dead weight."

The end of the rope with the fish tightly secured came to the surface. Bill pulled it toward him. Ike stepped down to the water's edge, as close as he could without his shadow falling on the stream. Carefully balancing himself, he reached toward the trout. His hand grasped the rope and he pulled it toward him.

"No wonder it pulled like a dead weight," he said.

"Why?" Pecos asked.

"Because it's a dead fish!" Ike replied.

"What?" Bill exclaimed, as he drew near.

Delicate streams of steam floated up from the fish. The delicious odor of cooking trout filled the air.

Ike touched the fish with an inquiring finger. "Ouch!" he exclaimed, as he drew his hand back quickly.

"What's the matter?" Bill asked.

"It's hot," said Ike.

"Let me see," said Bill. He reached for the trout and examined it closely. "Ike," he said, "this-here fish is cooked!"

"But, but . . ." stammered Three-fingered Ike, "how could that happen? It ain't bin nowhere near a fire. It's bin in water. Cold water!"

"No," said Bill seriously, as the truth slowly came to him. "It's bin in hot water. Boilin' hot water!"

"But right here is the river," Ike exploded. "An' it's cold!"

"It's cold on top," Bill answered. "But it's a fast river. You know that. It flows so fast it wore blisters on the buckskin's nose. An' it even wore away them tough whiskers on Widow Maker's nose. On top, there ain't nothin' but air fer the water to rub against. But on the bottom, it flows over rocks."

"Yes, but . . ."

"When it flows over the rocks, there is friction. An' friction makes heat. Everybody knows that. An' that water is flowin' so fast, it makes so much heat from the friction that the water starts a boilin'."

"Somehow it don't seem . . ."

"I know it don't. It don't seem quite right. But it is. It's as clear as kin be. The water on the bottom is boilin' hot. The hot water don't come to the top because the current is so fast it ain't got time. The result is there is cold water on top. That's where the fish live. They got to git their grub somehow. They cain't go to the bottom an' root around there. If they did, they'd all git boiled to death. That's why they was so hungry an' made such a fuss when they seen them worms I dug."

"Seems reasonable the way you tell it, Bill."

"Course it is. An' when I lassoed that trout, he dove down, tryin' to get away. Like they always do. He come to the boilin' water on the bottom an' he got himself cooked right then an' there. That was the reason he didn't fight none. Instead of fightin', he was cookin'."

Three-fingered Ike shuffled uneasily and scratched the rough thatch of hair back of his ear. There was a stubborn, worried look on his face that indicated to some extent the difficulty he was experiencing now that he had come face to face with the logic of it. But Bill was at ease with the evident truth. He was also hungry.

"What are we standin' here fer, waggin' our chins? We got some good, hot grub right in our hands. What are we waitin' fer?"

"I'll start a fire an' make some coffee," said Ike.

"Start a fire if you want to," Pecos said. "Jest git me the coffeepot an' we'll have hot coffee faster than a rabbit kin hop."

He tied the coffeepot to his lariat. He put coffee and a rock in the bottom and tossed it out into the stream. It sank with an explosive gurgle and settled down on the hot rocks at the bottom. The friction-heated water filled the pot. Bill could see it through the clear, swiftly running water. There was no doubt. It was boiling satisfactorily.

He left it there long enough to make it good and strong. Strong coffee for a strong man. Pecos Bill didn't like coffee that was strong enough to walk. Bill liked it just strong enough to push the sides of the coffeepot out a little.

Hot coffee and hot fresh trout for breakfast! Bill

and Ike sat by the strange stream in strange luxury. The sun was high now and Ike didn't have to worry about his shadow. It was less trouble than trying to serve hot flapjacks. All Pecos had to do was lasso a jumping trout, wait while the fish dove to the bottom and got itself cooked, pull it up and serve it piping hot.

"This here is real nice," said Bill, as he finished off half a trout and pulled in another, cooked to perfection. "An' real handy, too. I'm sorta glad we had to stay here to let that buckskin's nose git well."

Sourdough Special

It is well known that Pecos Bill invented everything connected with the cowpunching business. Many of Bill's inventions were perfect from the beginning, but several had to have one or two small improvements as times changed. It was a gradual process. In spite of what some people say, Bill was not perfect. He made mistakes once in a while. When he had to do something impossible, it sometimes took two or three tries.

Everyone knows about the shocking state of the cow business before Bill came. Cowhunts by cowboys. Men acting like boys. Bill changed that to roundups by cowpunchers. Men acting like men. Bill's inventions were real, and personal. He was not satisfied to tell others how things should be done. He did them himself.

Of course, his first thought was of his men. The roundup and the long drives made it necessary for the punchers to go out on the range for long periods of time. Cowpunchers could no longer go to the house for lunch, and to sleep, and to get out of the rain. They had to have a place to live and something to eat while they were out on the range. So Bill invented the chuck wagon.

Everything the men needed was in or on the chuck wagon. Pecos Bill's ingenuity was everywhere about it. There was the chuck box, fastened to the rear end of the wagon. Shelves, bins and drawers were built in it to hold the kitchen utensils and the eating-irons, the knives, forks, spoons, plates and cups. The chuck was also stored there.

The end of the chuck box was hinged at the bottom. When this lid was let down, it was held level by two legs and formed a table. It was a worktable for the cook, and was never used as a dining table.

At the front of the wagon, on the outside, was the jewelry chest. This was a storage box for extra hobbles, ammunition, rawhide, small tools, and other miscellaneous items important to the outfit's work.

A water barrel was in the wagon. Underneath was the cooney, a dried cowhide, slung like a hammock, and used for carrying fuel for the fire, wood or chips.

The chuck wagon! In it were loaded the cow-punchers' bedrolls and extra clothes. They slept near it. It was their hospital. It was the place where they swapped yarns and sang during the short hours between supper and time to turn in. It was the place where the cowpunchers lived when they were on the range. It was their home.

Busy, active, hard-working men need food. Lots of it. And good food. Bill knew how important grub is to cowpunchers. One of his greatest inventions was sourdough. That is, he didn't really invent it. It had been used for years, centuries. But he improved it. With such finesse, and so completely, that many people give him credit for being its inventor.

The sourdough Bill improved, invented, you might say, was improbable stuff. But then, even the old-fashioned kind was improbable, too. No one thought it would work. No one except Bill. Bill knew the power of Idaho potatoes. He knew the strength of the volcanic ash of the Idaho valleys that gave the potatoes their size and glorious taste.

So he started with Idaho potatoes. It was the natural consequence of an experience he once had at his Idaho ranch. He was the only rancher there at the time. Other than the Indians, and Bill's cow-punchers, the only men in the area were the mountain men, the trappers who braved the untamed mountains and the raging rivers trapping beaver.

Bill discovered there was something special about the potatoes that grew in Idaho. When they had plenty of water, they were unusual in size and character. But there was not always enough water. And he noticed that it took a good deal of the cook's time to wash the potatoes.

Time was important to Bill and he decided to see what he could do about it. He planted a row of onions between the rows of potatoes. The idea worked just as he had planned. The onion odors got in the potatoes' eyes. Tears came. At once there was plenty of water, and the potatoes grew with unusual abandon. The water supply was exactly right.

When the soil was dry, the sharp, tear-producing odors would seep through the soil. Water came to the potatoes' eyes and trickled out to the thirsty roots. The plants responded at once. The onion odors were shut off when the soil became saturated with water. Then the tears stopped. A natural, automatic way of irrigating potatoes. And when they were dug, having been well-washed, they always came out as clean as a hard-boiled egg.

Down at the far end of the patch, at the edge of the desert, there was one potato plant that wouldn't cry. No matter how hard the onions tried to produce tears, no tears would come.

Bill saw the unusual plant. No tears. No irrigation.

No water of any kind. But it was growing neverthe-less. He pinched the plant, but still there were no tears. No crybaby potato this.

He must have had something in mind from the beginning, because he told Bean Hole, the cook, "When I'm not around, I want you to take keer of that pertater plant. Jest give it a little water from the river, if it needs any. An' see that the weeds is kept down."

Bean Hole appreciated the honor of being singled out to perform an important task. "I'll take good keer of it, Pecos," he said.

"I don't think it'll need much attention. It's an unusually tough plant. It's my guess it'll git along without much water, an' it'll prob'ly kill all the weeds around it, an' the onions, too, fer that matter."

"Them's big, strong, red onions," Bean Hole said, doubtfully.

"I know. But that pertater plant is powerful, too. It kin take keer of itself," Bill replied. "Jest watch it, that's all."

The summer sped on and the potato plant grew. Grew better than those Bill had so cleverly irrigated. He usually stopped to see how the plant was doing as he rode in from the greasewood flats.

One night, Gun Smith saw that Bill was lost in thought. The big cowpuncher was squatting on his heels, aimlessly scratching in the dust with a piece of sage brush. Gun sauntered over.

"What's the trouble, Bill?" he asked.

"Gun, I got a terrible problem to figger out."

"I ain't much at figgers. I kin throw a figger-eight with a rope but that's about all. But I'd be glad to listen."

"I got a wonderful pertater growed, an' now I don't know what to do with it."

"Why?" Gun asked.

"It growed where it's real dry. Didn't hardly git no water at all. It's a strong pertater. It ain't no cry-baby, an' it wouldn't shed no tears like all the other pertaters did. Bean Hole tells me it even pulled its own weeds."

"That's a real unusual pertater. But I don't see that it should cause you no trouble. The more per-taters like that, the better. Save it fer seed."

"That's what I bin troubled about. If I save it fer seed, the world in the future will be a very different place."

"How's that?"

"There will be a race of pertaters that kin stand the dryest weather an' won't need no irrigatin'. An' not only that, but they will pull their own weeds."

"Seems like there ain't no other choice. Other than eatin' 'em, of course," Gun said.

"Yep, there is. An' that's the trouble," Bill replied, soberly.

"What other choice is there?" Gun asked.

"Sourdough."

"Sourdough?"

"Yep," said Bill with the quiet, grim concentration of genius. "Now I got a chance to improve sourdough. To make it a complete, finished product. But if I do, the world will never have desert-growin', weed-pullin' pertaters."

"That's right."

"Instead, it will have sourdough of artistic beauty. Sourdough that will go bubblin' an' workin' through the ages. Makin' biscuits an' flapjacks an' pan bread that will melt the heart, an' nourish the innards of mankind. Cowpuncher vittles that will romance with lick and pig's vest through all eternity."

"Fat bacon an' molasses go mighty good with sourdough biscuits right now. But I'm all ears. 'Cept your making me so hungry, it won't be long before I'll feel like I'm all stomach," Gun said.

"I'll do it!" Bill exclaimed explosively. "There ain't no two ways about it! Pertaters will still go on growin'. Folks will have to irrigate 'em if it don't rain. An' folks will have to pull the weeds, too. Anyway, I'm a cowpuncher, not a farmer. Sourdough comes first!"

"You got me curious," Gun said. "Jest what is it you're goin' to do?"

"I'm goin' to make the best sourdough in the world," Bill answered. "I'm goin' to grate them pertaters. All of 'em. Every one. It don't matter how special they might be fer seed. They're even more special fer sourdough. I ain't goin' to leave a single one fer seed."

At the sound of these dramatic words, and at the mention of sourdough, Bean Hole, the cook, approached.

Bill continued, with growing intensity. "I'm goin' to put 'em in a special keg. I'm goin' to put some water an' some sugar an' some yeast with 'em. There ain't no secret about how to make sourdough. The real secret is in havin' the right pertaters. Then I'm goin' to store it away at jest the right temperature, in jest the right place. When it's finally bubblin' and frothin', it'll make the best sourdough fodder anywhere. Them extra strong pertaters will keep it rich an' strong ferever."

Pecos made the mixture and put the keg in a small pantry in the corner of the cook shack. He said no more about it, but Bean Hole and Gun Smith saw that he watched the temperature carefully. On cold nights he took the keg to bed with him. Sudden changes in temperature and freezing spell disaster to sourdough. And even this strong and powerful sourdough could not stand too much frost.

Bean Hole's spatter-dab pancakes, biscuits and bread, made of old-fashioned sourdough, had always been his pride and joy. But he welcomed progress. He knew Pecos Bill's new sourdough would make the old kind obsolete. He waited for the improved product impatiently. "When's that new sourdough goin' to be ready?" he asked.

"If that stuff pans out right, everybody will know when it's finished," Bill replied. "I'm watchin' it all right. But my work is done. Now, it's a-workin'. We'll know when it's done all right."

He turned his attention to a little, brown, wild horse he had just caught. Bill had Widow Maker, Lightning and several others in his *remuda*. While the little, brown horse would be small for him, the bronco had style, stamina, courage and speed. Pecos Bill couldn't resist training a horse that seemed to be capable of greatness.

The answer to the cook's question was not long in coming. Bright, gurgling sounds came from the tightly-closed closet. Then one day the cowpunchers were hanging around the cook shack door, waiting for the dinner bell. They were all washed up, and the last one, Cuchillos y Agudos, was plastering down his shiny, black hair.

Bean Hole stepped to the iron wagon-wheel tire that served as a dinner bell. He picked up the branding iron that did double service as a tongue for the bell. He struck the tire. The melodious tone was submerged in a roar. A musical, resounding blast!

The sourdough exploded. The side of the cook shack disappeared in splinters. A gossamer spray of sourdough filled the air, defaced by splashes and blotches of the same powerful substance. It showered down over everything in the vicinity.

One of the things in the vicinity was the little brown bronco. He was almost covered with the creamy-white sourdough. Small brown spots remained uncovered. An extra heavy gob spattered on his nose. Globules ricocheted into his eyes. Blinded, he shook his head like a terrier shaking a rat. The stuff flew from his eyes. He could see again.

As he reared up in fright, the hackamore broke. He lit out of there fast and didn't stop until he came to the Palouse River country in Washington. The powerful sourdough bleached his hair and the uncovered spots remained dark. The eyes and nose got special treatment. Pink and white was the prevailing color.

The bronco was captured by the Nez Perce Indians, who had an eye for handsome horseflesh. And that mustang was the foundation father of the Apa-

loosa breed. American tongues tied themselves in knots trying to pronounce French. So a Palouse horse, a horse from the Palouse River country, became an Apaloosa to the American frontiersmen who had a stringhalt in the tongue when it came to pronouncing foreign words.

The mustang not only sired the beautiful, sturdy Apaloosa breed which is still distinguished by small spots of color on white, a pink nose, and white in the eye. He established the breed that distinguished the Nez Perce Indians when their remarkable Chief Joseph and a handful of braves managed to keep several thousand soldiers very busy for a long time during the Nez Perce war in 1877.

The mountain men, the fearless trappers of the unexplored West were having their rendezvous at the junction of the Snake and Bear Rivers. They heard the explosion over the two mountain ranges and, eager for excitement, headed for the scene.

By the time they arrived, Pecos Bill and the cowpunchers had repaired the damage and had rescued some of the potent sourdough and put it in jugs. Bill saw them approach with pleasure.

There was Peg-leg Smith, sometimes called the "Bald Hornet." A man whose tough nature and rugged courage was such that he amputated his own leg after it was horribly broken in a fight with Indians. Then he made his own wooden leg of an oak-tree limb and continued his dangerous calling in the mountain wilderness.

There was Jim Bridger who discovered the Yellowstone and its wonders. A man who could tell tales as well as he could hunt. And there was no better hunter.

There was Bill Williams who knew the Bible like he knew the endless mountain trails. He hunted and trapped alone. He loaded everything he needed on his battered horse, Rosinante, and went in quest of virgin beaver streams. He found them, too. Some people thought it was luck. But those who knew Old Bill Williams knew that luck had nothing to do with it.

There was Jedediah Strong Smith, who mixed exploring with trapping. Who had a memorable fight with a grizzly bear. The bear grabbed him with such force, the butcher knife strapped to Smith's side was broken. His face and head were cruelly lacerated by teeth and claws. But he won the fight. And he directed the stitching of his torn face with a needle and thread.

All the mountain men were there. Those known to history and those unknown. And there was a crew of savage Indians.

"You're jest in time fer a fiesta," said Bill as the motley crew of mountain men approached.

That was good news for the mountain men. After solitary, dangerous months alone in the unmapped wilderness, they were ready for a frolic.

"What you got planned, Bill?" Peg-leg Smith inquired.

"Sourdough biscuits," Bill replied.

"Wal, I'm always ready fer biscuits," Jim Bridger said. "But it 'pears to me that ain't no great shucks. We use sourdough every day. Couldn't hardly git along without it."

"Yep. I know," Bill answered. "But these biscuits are goin' to be different. You never tasted anything like these before."

The mountain men were unimpressed, even though they knew they could expect the unusual from Pecos Bill. Sourdough was sourdough to them.

"That's real thoughtful of you, Pecos," Jim Bridger said. "An' we are hungry."

"Git ready then," Bill said. "The boys will do some bronco bustin' an' some rope spinnin' so's you kin pass the time 'til dinner's ready. You kin arrange some shootin' matches, too."

Pecos turned to Bean Hole. "Let's git goin'," he said. "We got a lot of work to do."

Fiesta for Mountain Men

COOKING was a man's work at Hell's Gate Gulch and any other self-respecting outfit in the old West. Cowpuncher, mountain man, guide, hunter, gold digger or mule skinner had to know how to cook, if he wanted to eat. Eating, of course, is common practice with everyone, except angels. And there were few angels in the early West.

Bill went at his task with energy and enthusiasm. Gun Smith, Alkali Ike, Three-fingered Ike, Cuchillos y Agudos and Bean Hole received their instructions and carried them out. It was not long until fires were built and sides of beef, loins of antelope, buffalo humps and beaver tails were sizzling happily, filling the air with a delicious aroma.

Son-of-a-gun stew was bubbling merrily in the big, black pot. Son-of-a-gun stew! What a dish! The easiest dish in the world to make, according to Bill's own recipe: "Take a small quantity of water. Add all the leftovers available. Add one calf, finely chopped. Include everything except the horns, the hide and the holler. Simmer until done. Eat until done."

Other cowpunchers could make good son-of-a-gun stew, too. There was artistry in choice of ingredients, preparation and cooking. Pecos Bill's test was in the eating. "It ain't real son-of-a-gun stew if you kin tell what's in it," he always said.

Bill personally mixed his new sourdough with the flour and made the biscuit dough. And he personally put the biscuits in the oven. Everything had to be exactly right.

When everything was ready, Bean Hole lifted the branding iron and hit the iron tire. The musical sound told the cowpunchers and the mountain men that dinner was ready. They came. Hungry, hardy men, ready for one of life's noblest experiences— eating a well-prepared meal.

Pecos and the cook watched happily as rough cowboys and fierce mountain men and Indians attacked the waiting food.

"Hey, Pecos. Where's them sourdough biscuits?" shouted Peg-leg Smith.

"Comin' right up. Good an' hot," said Pecos. He flipped them out of the pan on a big tray, lifted it lightly above his head with a flourish, balanced on one hand.

He paused, "This-here is my invention. This-here is real, throat-ticklin' grub," he said.

"An' I'm jest itchin' to line my flue with it," Peg-leg roared.

Pecos lowered the tray with another flourish. All eyes followed its course.

"There ain't nothin' on that tray!" Jim Bridger exclaimed.

Bill looked down. True. The tray was empty. The smile on his face melted into a puzzled frown. What could have happened? He looked on the ground. Perhaps the biscuits had slipped off. But they were not there. They were gone. But where? Suddenly, Bill knew what had happened. He looked up.

"There they are!" he said, pointing at the sky. "There go the sourdough biscuits!" He pointed toward the tops of the cottonwoods that edged the river bank. "Them sourdough biscuits is so light, they jest naturally up an' floated away on the breeze!"

A gasp of doubt arose. It died as the crowd looked up and confirmed the strange fact. The cream-colored biscuits, with wrinkles of golden brown, were floating in the blue sea of the sky. Floating away.

"Wal, Bill, I wouldn't have believed it if I hadn't seen it myself," Jim Bridger exclaimed. "An' I've seen some strange things in my day. But you're right! You're talkin' jest as straight as a wagon tongue."

"Bill," said Peg-leg Smith, "us mountain men don't awe easy. I've seen about everything, but I swear I'm awful awed. I'm also hungry. You promised us some sourdough biscuits. An' I want 'em. But no one kin eat them biscuits 'cept birds, an' I ain't no bird."

Pecos' hands dropped to his hips. There was a quick movement. His guns were in his hands. A roar filled the air. Smoke drifted down.

Sharp ears heard the twelve shots that to slower ears seemed to be one continuous sound. Sharp eyes noticed that the heavy smoke sank down to the ground while the light sourdough biscuits were going up. All eyes saw twelve holes appear in twelve, distant, floating sourdough biscuits.

"Cain't let no air out of them biscuits," said Gun Smith. "What you got now is sourdough doughnuts. An' they're floatin' away."

"Don't let it bother you none," Jim Bridger said. "This steak is real tender. It's so tender I don't see how it held the cow together."

"What you goin' to do now, boss?" asked Bean Hole, in a worried voice.

"There's more biscuits cookin'," Bill replied. "Git 'em. An' put a lid over 'em so's they cain't float away. I'll cook up some more that will be heavy enough to stay down where they belong."

Bean Hole took the rest of the biscuits from the fire. He put plates on top of them and handled the tray gently. No more flourishes! The lesson had been learned. With Pecos Bill's new, improved, extra-light sourdough biscuits, one did not flourish the tray. One covered it. One grabbed a biscuit quickly, but firmly, and then kept a good hold, so it couldn't float away.

The next batch was an even greater success. Bill, with his usual sharpness of mind, put berries in the dough. The slight but tasty weight of the berries was just enough to keep the biscuits from flying off into outer space. Just enough, too, to aid the delicacy in nestling down in exactly the right inner space in the hungry men.

"I've said a lot of mean things about sourdough biscuits in my day," Jim Bridger said. His taste buds were working so hard they overflowed and tears came to his eyes. Tears of sheer gustatory joy. "I've called them hot rocks."

Confession was in the air. "I've called 'em sinkers,"

Peg-leg Smith said. "But these not only reach my stomach, they fill my heart with goodness. They even soften the wood in my peg leg."

"I've called them millstones," said Three-fingered Ike.

"Me, I used to call 'em bullets," said Gun Smith, caressing a bit of biscuit tenderly with the inside of his Adam's apple, as it floated past on its way to fulfill the great and good mission of a sourdough biscuit.

Supper was over. The cowpunchers, the mountain men and the Indians sat around the fire. Everyone sang a song, told a story, or danced a jig. Everyone except Pecos Bill and Three-fingered Ike.

There was a pause, a long pause. The fire had burned down to a blanket of glowing embers. There was silence. A silence that was broken by Pecos Bill.

"I ain't had," he said, "such a time since I was a coyote."

There was silence. Thundering silence. Every man had heard that Bill grew up with the coyotes.

"Yes," Pecos said, at length, "I had some great times when I was a coyote. Only one thing I wish. I wish I knowed somethin' about what happened to me when I was real young."

"You mean it?" asked Three-fingered Ike.

"Shore I mean it."

"Wal," said Three-fingered Ike. "I knowed you when you was a leetle shaver. I was huntin' buffalo then. Fightin' Injuns too, of course. I seen you lots of times. I knowed yore Grammaw an' Grampaw. Come over the Cumberland Gap with 'em. I knowed yore Paw an' yore Maw back on the Washitaw River. Hunted bar in the canebrakes with yore ole' man, an' wrassled alligators with him on the mud flats. Real good alligator wrassler, he was. Good bar hunter likewise."

"Did he ever hunt bar like Pecos done when he was a coyote?" asked Bronco Jones.

"Nope. Not that way. Guess no one else ever done it that way," Three-fingers said.

"Why didn't you ever tell me that you knowed me when I was a young'un?" Bill asked.

"You never asked me," said Ike quietly. "An' like you know, out West here, we never talk about people, unless we're asked to. We know when to speak our mind, and when to mind our speech."

"I lost my memory way back when I was a young 'un. I don't remember nothin' that happened before I was bounced out of a wagon on a rock on my head," said Bill. "I'd like to know what happened in those early days. And I'd like to know now."

Three-fingered Ike's Story

THREE-FINGERED Ike hunched up his shoulders. The glow of the burning embers cast a soft light on his rugged old face. There was character in every line and wrinkle. It was clear that he was a truthful man. He was so honest he couldn't lie without telling the truth. With simple frankness and clarity he told about Bill's early life.

"Wal," said Ike, "the West was wild before Pecos Bill showed up on the scene. I lived in it, an' I know. But a mighty strange thing happened on the night he was foaled. The West began to git a leetle bit fuzzy at the edges."

He turned to face Bill. "You was borned at the edge of the West, on the slopes of the Sabine River,

on the Texas Border. The fuzz growed long an'
shaggy there. It wasn't long before it became woolly
all over, an' it has been wild an' woolly ever since.

"You always went after everything like there wasn't
no time to waste. You was crawlin' in two an' a half
days, an' you was up to yore neck in mischief before
the third day was over. Yore Maw give you Jim
Bowie's famous knife to cut yore teeth on. She
raised up seventeen other young 'uns before Bill
here," Ike said impressively as he turned to include
the others, "an' she could be classed as an expert."

"That was a purty big family," said Bronco Jones.

"That it was," Ike agreed. "Wal, sir, one day she
got a gourd. The biggest one she could find, an' she
filled it with rocks. She run an old ax helve through
the middle, an' what did she have then?" Ike looked
at Curly.

"Gosh, Ike, I don't know. What was it?" Curly
asked.

"She had a rattle, that's what. And Bill he took to
it right off. But he only liked it fer a few hours. Then
he throwed it away. Too babyfied for him.

"I was visitin' with Bill's folks jest then, durin' a
leetle pause between Injun wars. I helped his Maw
make the rattle. So we was talkin' there, Paw an'
Maw an' me, an' one of the oldest girls I was kind of
sweet on. First thing we knows, there was Bill, he

was rollin' an' empty sorghum barrel away from the side of the cabin. Maw says to the young 'un, 'Put that there sorghum barrel back,' she says. An' he done it, right off."

"He minded good, eh?" Gun Smith asked.

"He shore did. He done everything he was told to do right away. Wasn't like some of the young 'uns these days. So Bill jest crawled off toward a tribe of Injuns that was passin' by."

"Injuns?" asked Bronco Jones. "Between Injun wars? Seems like that might of been sort of dangerous."

"Bill could take keer of himself, we figgered, so Maw she went off to chop some wood to cook dinner with an' Paw an' me went along to watch her. Jest to keep her company, you know, while she was doin' her work. There wasn't no need to do nothin' about the young 'un. He was doin' all right, adjustin' himself to his surroundin's, an' all.

"Wal, sir, before long the noise of Maw's choppin' ax cuttin' against the choppin' block was drownded out by a racket that filled the clearin'. Maw picked up her ax firm-like, an' she headed fer the noise. I lifted my rifle, but I was more cautious-like, Injuns bein' around an' all."

"Was the Injuns on the warpath?" asked Bean Hole.

"You would of thought so, from all the noise. But nope, that wasn't it."

"What was it?"

"That's what I'm tellin' you," Ike said. "We rounded the corner of the shack an' there we seen Bill. He was a-poundin' on a rattle of his own choice an' manufacture. There he was, with a stick in each hand, poundin' on the top of an Injun war drum like he was gettin' ready to go on the warpath with the Comanches."

" 'Ain't that cute,' says Maw. 'I s'pose that somehow he traded the Injuns out of that drum.'

" 'But,' says I, 'there's somethin' else, besides a plain ole Injun war drum.'

" 'You bet,' says Paw. 'That noise is fiercer, an' more vicious than an Injun war drum. It's got a quaverin' tone that sounds real mean.'

" 'By cracky, Paw, yore right!' Maw shouted. 'It's makin' my blood run cold, an' no plain ole Injun war drum ever done that!'

"Then she turned to me. 'Got yore shootin' iron ready, Ike?' she says.

"Yep," says I, "an' I don't mind tellin' you that I wondered what good it was, 'cause I didn't know what I'd have to shoot. She went right up to that drum, an' I follered her, an' through the lacin' on the drumhead we seen a dozen rattlesnakes inside the drum. They was writhin' an' squirmin' an' hissin' an' rattlin' an' bangin' their tails against the drum."

"What do you know!" exclaimed Gun Smith.

"Yep. Somehow Bill had corralled them critters an' put 'em to work helpin' him beat the drum.

"Well, sir, you know, Maw didn't say nothin' all the way home. She was figgerin'. Late that night I was layin' in my soogans along with all the boys in camp, lookin' at the stars through the chinks in the cabin walls, an' I calculated she didn't like the idea of young Bill wandering around loose. And sure enough she figgered somethin' out.

"First thing in the mornin' she gathered the ole man, an' me, an' the boys around, an' she says, 'We're goin' to make that young'un a cradle. A cradle that's good an' strong an' will keep him safe and out of mischief.'

"The ole man, he answers right up. 'No cradle ever seen will do the trick,' he says.

"Mebby we could hobble him in the wagon box," I says, 'cause I was figgerin' to go out an' scout me out a herd of buffalo.

"'It ain't big enough,' she says. 'Now, you-all jest do as I say, an' I don't want no arguments.'

"Wal, sir, all of us boys knew who ran things around that clearin', so we jest listened an' done like she said.

" 'First off,' she says, 'git me four good stout logs. Real stout ones now. An' git me all the Mexican iron you kin lay yore hands on.'

"We went an' got four pine logs. Hard pine they was. An' we got a lot of Mexican iron. Then we began to work on a cradle."

"How big was them logs, Ike?" Bronco Jones asked.

"Oh, about as big as my leg, thick, that is. They was nice long springy pieces of timber," Ike answered. "So there was all the stuff. We lashed the logs together with the rawhide, an' we wove rawhide back an' forth like springs on the bottom. We lashed a decent railin' on the sides an' covered the bottom with bearskins and buffalo robes.

"Maw was pleased. 'That will hold him,' she says.

"The ole man wasn't sure we'd used enough Mexican iron on the bottom. But Maw she said, 'Mexican iron is real tough. It don't break an' don't never wear out.' Then she called to mind how we used it to tie the wagon wheels together an' fer shoein' the cow an' the hosses an' makin' harness an' snakin' logs.

" 'Course, she was right. There ain't nothin' hardly that will stand up to good rawhide. Wal, we rigged a block an' tackle an' soon that cradle was swingin' between two live-oak trees, about forty feet off the ground.

" 'What do you want to corral him so high up fer?' asked the ole man.

" 'I don't want him to get out,' Maw says. 'I want him to be safe from harm.' She was a real good mother, she was. She'd go to a lot of trouble fer her young 'uns. She looked up there so fond-like as that cradle lurched back and forth in the high wind. Her eyes sort of glistened as she seen Bill's head over the railin'. She was real happy that young'un was safe from harm.

"When we looked up, we could see the movement of his feet as he ran around chasin' birds. When he went to sleep, we could see a reassurin' bump in the bottom of the cradle, with the rawhide strips stretched tighter than the short strings of an angel's harp. It was a real impressive sight, I can tell you. Can you imagine, that baby's bottom that was stretchin' that rawhide so tight was the same bottom that in later days made Death Valley?"

"How long did he use the cradle?" asked Gun Smith.

"I bet not very long," said Bronco Jones.

"Yo're right, Bronco. I don't jest remember how long, but not very long. One mornin' bright an' early Maw started hollerin'. 'Course all of us went a-runnin'. I looked up an' I seen what was the matter. That firm, reassurin' bump in the bottom of the cradle was gone. Somehow, he had got out!"

"Climbed down the tree, I bet," said Bean Hole.

"Nope. There wasn't no marks or scratches on the trunk. Anyway, the tree was too big. Bill couldn't get his arms around them. He might grow up thinkin' he was a coyote, an' actin' sometimes like there was some wild cat in him, but he couldn't git down that tree."

"Mebby he was carried away by eagles or buzzards," Gun Smith suggested.

"Nope. I thought of that at the time. I figgered he jest grabbed on to some birds and was flown away. It was Maw who found out what had happened. 'Here,' she says. 'He's jumped out.'"

"'Fell, hey?' said I."

"'Nope, he jumped,' she says. 'He doesn't do things by accident. He done it on purpose. He jumped.'

"You could see how the ground under the cradle was all packed down where he hit the ground. 'Look,' says Maw, pointin' at a flat across the gully. 'He's over there playin'.'

"We climbed the rocks back of the cabin where we could git a good view. 'Listen to him laugh,' says the ole man.

"'There, look at that cloud of dust,' she says. 'That's him.' The dust was swirlin' around the scrubby ground in wide curves. When the dust floated away, we could see him.

" 'He's bein' drug over the ground by four badgers!' Bill had hold of two badger tails between the fingers of each hand, like an overland stage driver holdin' the reins of a four-horse team. 'They look like awful unhappy badgers,' says I.

"Maw yelled at him. Bill dug his leetle heels into the rocky ground an' pulled his team to a halt. She yelled at him to come home, so he pulled his team around. He hollered at 'em an' his team was off, and in less time than a bull calf takes to switch his tail they headed down into the trees in the gully an' out of sight.

" 'I s'pose, I should give him a strappin', but I don't like to. He's so sensitive,' she says.

" 'I say, forget about the cradle,' says Paw. 'Let him run loose if that's what he wants to do.'

" 'I got to say,' she says, 'it was a real purty picture seein' him drug over them rocks an' sandburr patches.'

" 'I wonder where he is,' says I.

" 'You kin hear him hollerin' down in the gully,' says Maw. 'Maybe he's stopped to ketch some more badgers.'

" 'Hi up! Hi up!' Bill yelled, down in the gully. He sounded like a mule skinner tryin' to git a eight-mule team to lay into their collars. We could see the treetops shakin' as he bumped against their trunks.

" 'Here he comes,' says the ole man.

" 'Yep, there's the noses of six critters in that dust comin' up over the edge of the gully,' says I. We could see the six noses, then six heads and then, as they came farther out of the dust, six bodies.

" 'Sakes alive,' Maw cried. 'He didn't ketch two more badgers. He ketched two skunks!'

"Bill pulled his team to a halt. He let go of six very sore, unhappy tails, an' six unhappy critters took advantage of their freedom an' hightailed it in six different directions.

"Me an' the ole man was laughin' like all get-out, but Maw, she didn't laugh none. She jest looked at Bill, and she says, 'You jest crawl right back down to the crick an' wash yoreself good. An' don't you come back until you smell better. You kin howl like a coyote if you want to. You kin yowl like a wild cat if you think you got to, but no one in my family can be a skunk! Can't even smell like one!'

"Me an' the ole man scared the grins off our chins. It did seem funny, but she was right an' we didn't argue with her none. We wouldn't have argued with her even if she was wrong. A body didn't argue with Maw. Not if he knew what was good fer him.

"But me an' the ole man talked it over an' we made some decisions. So that night the ole man says to her, he says, 'I guess I better take that young'un out huntin' with me.'

" 'He ain't old enough,' she says.

" 'He's sturdy enough,' says I.

" 'An' he's fast enough,' says the ole man.

" 'An' it'll keep him out of mischief,' I adds my two-cents' worth."

Three-fingered Ike stood up and stretched. He took a step toward the fire. "There's more I could tell, Pecos," he said. "But it's gettin' late. Mebby some other time I'll tell some more, if you want me to. But right now I figger we ought to be thinkin' that we got a long hard day on the trail tomorrow."

"Ike, I shore do appreciate knowin' some of the things that happened before I became a coyote. An' sometime, I may ask you to tell me some more."

"I'll be glad to," said Ike simply. "An' there is lots more to be told, because things moved purty fast in them old days."

The cowpunchers were speechless. Breathless. They had heard tales of real history that night on the trail. Everyone of them knew it. As they crawled into their blankets and gazed at the prairie moon for a few minutes before sleep came, they thought of the old times and the old days when Pecos Bill was young.

Rat and the Rustlers

THE ROUNDUP was over. Pecos Bill's Hell's Gate Gulch outfit had cut out the trail herd and started the long drive north. It was the second night on the trail. Everything had gone well. The snuffy steers leading the trail herd had settled down to a pace slow enough for the drags. The herd was bedded down. The trail hands, except the night guard, were gathered around the campfire near the chuck wagon.

The cowpunchers had been singing, as cowpunchers do in the evening between chow and time to crawl into the bedrolls. Pecos Bill, as everyone should know, was a great singer. He was the greatest yipper and yapper in the coyote world when he was a coyote. "Yippee!", the word so important to cowboy songs, was one of his greatest inventions. A word that means all things to all cows. A word that came straight from the coyotes. A word that has done so much to make cowboy songs what they are. And it must never be forgotten that Pecos Bill invented cowboy songs.

"Boys," said Bill, in a pause between songs, "there was rustlers workin' down there in the south part of the range. This-here trail herd is trail broke now. We bin over the willows twice. And swimmin' the herd is about as bad a job as you'll have. There won't be much trouble fer a few days. Probably nothin' at all, 'cept some redskins maybe. They might attack and give you a fight. But that won't bother you much."

"Might be a few renegades, an' maybe a stampede or so," Gun Smith suggested.

"Why, shore," Pecos agreed. "Little things like that. But you got to expect them things on the trail. You kin take keer of them all right."

The hands listened attentively. Bill continued, "I bin figgerin' that I ought to go back and tend to them rustlers. Gun, I want you to come with me. Cuchillos, that will leave you in charge. You'll be the trail boss 'till me an' Gun ketches up with you. That will be 'bout a week, at the most. Depends on how much trouble we have in trailin' down them rustlers. Jest keep the herd with their noses pointin' at the north star. Then you won't lose the trail."

Cuchillos y Agudos accepted the responsibility with a grin. Gun Smith bore his pride with grace and dignity. A cowpuncher couldn't help being proud when asked to accompany Pecos Bill on a search for rustlers. He was to be a one-man posse for Pecos Bill. Such an exploit would give him fame in the cow country and would very likely earn him a place in history. Gun Smith was grateful.

"Now," said Bill, "it's time to hit the soogans."

"Yep," Gun agreed, stretching his great frame in a satisfying yawn. "It's the prairie feathers fer me."

The hands got their bedrolls out of the bed wagon and in a few minutes the silence of sleep settled down on the camp. Long, deep sleep, unbroken by the cries of coyotes or the refrains of the night guard as the cowboys on watch slowly circled the herd.

Bill and Gun got up early. Stars were still twinkling in the sky. There was no light on the horizon to mark the place where the morning sun would rise. The only sign of life in camp was a pleasant one. The campfire was burning. Bean Hole was up. A good camp cook never lets a man start the day hungry. Or finish it hungry, either. And Bean Hole was a good cook. Hot coffee, sourdough biscuits, beans and pig's vest. A breakfast fit for a cowpuncher. A breakfast that would stick to the ribs and last out the morning's hard ride.

The two men roped their horses and saddled up.

Bean hole could see their silhouettes against the sky
that was slowly being washed light by the coming
sun. He raised his hand in answer to their gesture
of farewell and watched them fade into the prairie.

Bill and Gun rode fast. Rat, Bill's rattlesnake, was
cold and inactive for the first few miles. But after
the prairie sun arose, his rattles warmed up and he
rattled and hissed most of the morning. By early
afternoon he became tired and settled down for a
quiet, peaceful ride, as Bill had no occasion to use
him as a quirt.

"There's a rustler sign," said Bill, pointing at a small scar near the bottom of a low hill a quarter of a mile away. Without another word the men turned their horses toward the slope.

When they reached the place Bill had indicated, they found the remains of an old fire. "This-here is where they done some brand changin'," Bill observed.

"It's a purty old trail," Gun said. "It would be hard to foller."

"It might take a little time," Bill replied, "but it wouldn't be hard. This camp ain't more than three or four weeks old. We won't have no trouble."

Gun stepped down from his horse. He examined the burnt ends of the greasewood sticks that remained. "It looks to me like this trail is real cold," he said.

Bill could see that Gun was tired and that he probably would never be able to follow him along the month-old trail of the rustlers. "Guess you're right, Gun," he said cheerfully. "We kin find a warmer trail than that. Let's fergit the rustlers fer right now, and ride to Hell's Gate Gulch. It ain't very fur and we kin all use a real, good rest before we start after them rustlers."

"Anything you say, Bill," Gun replied, greatly relieved that the hunt was to be delayed for the night.

Pecos had sought to ease any feeling of inferiority Gun might have, which was apparent in his evident eagerness to put off the search for the rustlers. "It would take us a long time to follow that trail and cover all the ground them rustlers has bin coverin' durin' the past month," he said, as they rode toward the ranch. "I got to admit I'm tired. A good night's sleep will do us both good."

Gun Smith heard the words. He knew Pecos Bill was tireless. That he could track the rustlers down on the cold trail and never stop once. He knew that Bill was stopping for the night for his benefit alone. But he appreciated Bill's thoughtfulness, and the fierce loyalty he had for the big cowpuncher burned brightly. It was the sense of loyalty that sprang into full flame years before when he, then a murderous bad man, had leveled his guns in hate at young Pecos Bill, and had met defeat. Nothing had ever been said about the incident. But the memory of Bill's first day at Hell's Gate Gulch remained with Gun Smith.

Bill continued, as they rode slowly along. "Anyway, the hosses need a rest. I always say it ain't right to push good hoss flesh too fur." He protected his men and was always thoughtful of his beasts of burden.

It was late when they reached Hell's Gate Gulch.

The ranch house was dark and silent. The men who were not on the trail were out on the range. They unsaddled their horses, had a quick supper, and turned in.

The moon was high in the sky. Its pale glow cast a short, blunt, square of light on the floor near the bunkhouse wall.

Sleep came and the hours passed. Suddenly, the silence of the prairie night was shattered by an unearthly racket. Gun rose in his bunk and, leaning on his elbow, reached for his six-shooter. In the half-darkness across the room, he could see that Pecos was already alert.

"What is it?" he whispered. Bill moved closer. Gun Smith threw aside the blankets and stood near him.

"Don't know what it is," Bill replied softly. "But whatever it is, it's sure makin' a racket. There's more noise out there than a million tin cans droppin' on a flock of quackin' ducks."

"What you goin' to do, Bill?" Gun asked, in an excited whisper.

"I'm goin' to see what it is," Pecos replied. Six-gun in hand, he started slowly forward toward the noise, toward the door that led to the long gallery at the side of the house. Gun Smith followed and drew up behind Bill as he reached the door.

"You with me?" Bill asked.

"Right here."

"Good. Don't shoot if you don't have to," said Bill. "See what it is first." The noise, loud from the beginning, seemed to grow even louder. There was a sense of urgency about it.

"Can't you make out what it is?" Gun asked softly.

"Not yet. It ain't like nothin' I ever heard before. And it's gettin' louder. Sounds somethin' like a rattler. But not quite. More like a herd of skeletons doin' a hoedown on a tin roof. Wal, we'll soon find out jest what it is."

Bill's hand reached for the door. In his other hand, the muzzle of his lead-pusher glinted dangerously in the soft moonlight. Gun Smith's forty-five was ready too. He was serene and secure with a gun in his hand. But he could not help but notice that the barrel of his big companion's weapon bore in its cold silence and its alert angle a threat that his own could not equal. A rattler ready to strike. A panther to spring. A scorpion to sting. Pecos Bill's silent six-gun spoke all these. It spoke of death.

Pecos opened the door slowly. The shrill, rough rasp of the hinges could be heard in spite of the louder, coarser sound beyond. But the hinges sounded no warning. The cacophony continued unabated; indeed with a new, fresh vigor.

Bill stepped out on the porch. Gun Smith followed. Their eyes and their guns swept over the long, open gallery and centered on the third post from the end. A few quick steps forward dispelled the confusion created by the half-light, the continuing clatter and the excited scuffling of black shadows.

The scuffling stopped. Voices, pleading voices, arose in a duet, "Don't shoot! Don't shoot!"

The rattling and the banging ceased. The hissing faded into the night.

"Look at that, would you!" Pecos Bill exclaimed.

"What is it?" Gun asked, coming closer.

"It's Rat. It's that rattlesnake of mine," said Bill. "He has gone and captured a couple of fellers who must have come here fer no good purpose."

"How do you s'pose he done it?"

"From what I kin see, it's purty easy to make out what happened. Them fellers sneaked in, or was goin' to. There is the window they opened. Rat seen 'em, and he crawled up and wropped hisself around both of 'em. When he got 'em hog-tied, he jest wropped his neck around that porch post to hold 'em. See. That snake has got hisself half-hitched around the post. He took a dally welta on the post." Bill pondered for a moment. "But maybe not. Maybe Rat is a hard and fast roper. Maybe he tied hisself around the post first and then roped the varmints."

"Anyway," said Gun, as he stepped forward for closer inspection, "the rattler sure roped the critters."

"Ain't no doubt about that," Bill agreed.

"But where did all the noise come from?"

"Why Rat done that, too. After he got them two *hombres* lassoed, you'd think he done about everything a snake could be expected to do. But he didn't stop at that. He called fer help, which lots of folks might think would be kind of difficult fer a rattler to do. And he done it by rattlin' his tail real loud and bangin' it on the floor and porch rail."

"Look at that pore critter's tail! It's all bruised from the beatin' he give it. But Bill, who do you s'pose these varmints are that ole Rat has ketched?"

Rat had relaxed his hold somewhat and the two men, still firmly held in the loosened coils, stood in sullen silence. The danger of quick gunplay appeared to be past. There were no more frantic pleas for safety.

Bill faced the prisoners. "Who are you, strangers? And what you doin' here in the night time?"

There was no answer.

Bill's voice and face were stern. "I want an answer. Quick."

One of the men replied. "I ain't goin' to say nothin'."

"You can't prove nothin'," the other added.

"Let's finish 'em off," said Gun, taking a firmer grip on his revolver.

"No. We cain't do that," Bill replied.

" 'Course you can't," said the taller of the two. "You're Pecos Bill. An' everyone knows you don't shoot unless a man starts to draw on you first."

"Yeah," the other added, "an' we ain't goin' to draw. So there ain't nothin' you kin do!"

It was true. The men were clever. Pecos Bill would never shoot unless a man reached for his gun first.

"What are we goin' to do?" Smith asked.

"We got to follow the law," Bill replied. "I ain't goin' to shoot 'cept in strict accordance with the law. We got to git evidence. And after we git it, we got to take 'em before Judge Roy Bean, where they kin be tried, accordin' to law, before they kin be hung."

Pecos was the first Marshal of the Southwest. He was the first Texas Ranger. It was he who first brought law and order to a lawless, orderless land. He would follow the law. He would stop at nothing in his efforts to bring justice to the West. Prompt justice whenever possible.

"I ain't really no detective," Bill said. "I'm jest a cowhand and law enforcement officer whenever it's necessary. But, let's see. These *hombres* both have an iron rod in their hands. And they bin a-beatin' that pore snake with 'em.

"Firstly: that's cruelty to animals. A very serious criminal offense.

"Secondly: they used them same irons to pry open the window. Here is the marks on the window sill. They was usin' them irons as jimmies. That's possessin' and usin' burglar tools fer the unlawful purpose of breakin' and enterin' in the night time. That's a more serious crime, punishable by a necktie party.

"Thirdly: them same irons is runnin' irons, a deevice used fer changin' brands, the possession of which is *prima facie* evidence of a crime. And there ain't no more serious crime in the cow country than rustlin' cows! 'Cept fer hoss stealin'. And," he added in a matter of fact way, "the pains and penalties fer cattle rustlin' is also lookin' up a cottonwood limb from the end of a rope."

"Then what are we waitin' fer?" Gun exclaimed. "That's proof enough. We jest as good as caught 'em ridin' under a cottonwood limb. Both of 'em has bin packin' sticky ropes. They're the brand artists who have bin workin' ahead of our roundup."

He turned to Pecos and shouted, "Let that snake turn them snakes loose. Make 'em reach fer their guns. Them maverickers needs justice. Sudden justice! And I say we kin do justice without no Judge Roy Bean. All we got to do is to start burnin' a little powder!"

The two men were visibly affected by the logic

of Pecos Bill's deductions and his recitation of their offenses and the punishment in store for them. They were even more affected by the simple frontier logic and the incisive action urged by Gun Smith. But they were men who had long lived outside the law. Their first instinct was to use the forms and procedures of the law for improper ends. For delay.

One of them cleared his throat of the fear that choked him. He knew he stood in the presence of Pecos Bill. A bad man with a gun, but a peace officer, bound to law and to duty. In his heart, the rustler knew he deserved no mercy, no delay. But with his voice he said, "You can't do it. It wouldn't be lawful. We're entitled to a trial, witnesses, a judge, a jury, an' all the trimmin's."

Bill answered Gun's hard words softly, almost gently. "He's right, Gun. We cain't take the law in our own hands."

"But Bill," Gun implored, "it don't make sense. Roy Bean most likely won't do nothin' more than shake a rope at 'em. Jest warn 'em an' let 'em go. We kin take keer of it right!"

"No," Bill said flatly. "Leave loose of 'em, Rat." The rattler uncoiled and eased down to the porch floor and slid close to the wall where he would be out of the way if lead started to fly. Rat was a snake with considerable discretion.

The robbers stood stiff and motionless. "Do you want me to take their artillery?" Gun asked.

"No," Bill replied easily. "Ain't no use in that. Let 'em keep their hardware."

Gun nodded knowingly. The imperceptible exchange of glances revealed that the prisoners also understood. Bill had deliberately let them keep their guns, knowing he could outdraw them if they were so foolish as to start slapping their hips. Perhaps he even hoped for such an ill-advised move. But the rustlers would take no chances.

"Bill," said the bolder of the two, "my arms is stiff. I want to stretch 'em."

"Go ahead," Bill replied.

"My fingers needs stretchin', too. But they ain't itchin'. I ain't reachin'," he added cautiously.

"I kin tell an itchin' finger when I see one. Stretch all over if you want to. But I'll be ahead of you if you start diggin' fer lightnin'!"

The prisoners relaxed and eased their tired, stiff muscles, making sure to avoid any motion that might bring Bill's guns into action.

"Now, Gun, git a couple of piggin' strings so's we kin hog-tie these two poor specimens of crowbait."

Now that it seemed clear they were not to be shot in their tracks, the fear that had controlled the two rustlers disappeared and they were able to smile sardonically. It would be many days and nights before they could be delivered at the bar of Judge Roy Bean's court in the Jersey Langtry saloon, at Langtry. There was little reason to expect anything but quick, western justice there. But in the meantime, there would be chances for treachery and escape. They had done well. There was still hope.

Gun Smith turned and went into the house for the necessary ropes. The bark of two guns destroyed the silence. Gun rushed from the house, his own weapon ready. He saw Pecos Bill blowing the smoke from his gun barrels. A short distance away lay the two rustlers, each neatly drilled through the heart.

"What happened, Bill? What happened?" Smith shouted. "Did they draw on you?"

"No," said Bill. "They was too smart fer that."

"Bill, certainly you didn't . . ."

"No. I shot 'em good and lawful. Had to do it to uphold the dignity and the processes of the law. Them fellers wouldn't try to escape if there was any chance of 'em gettin' caught. They knowed it is lawful to shoot an escapin' prisoner."

"Then, what happened?"

"What they didn't know, is that it is also unlawful to resist an officer. That's what they done. They resisted an officer."

"What did they do?"

"I told 'em to stand up against the wall, and they didn't do it. That's resistin'. There wasn't nothin' else left fer me to do," he said, almost sadly. "They was took with a sudden case of lead poisonin'."

Now that the excitement was over, Rat moved away from the wall and edged out on the porch where the first rays of the morning sun were warming the rough boards. He began to nurse his battered tail. He spent the rest of the morning licking his tail and dozing to regain the sleep lost during the night. The treatment was successful and by the time the men were ready to ride up the trail, he was quite himself again.

The End of the Trail

Two days later, Pecos Bill and Gun Smith joined the trail herd. That evening after chow, while Pecos was riding night herd, there was no singing around the campfire. The hands listened to Gun's story of the adventure with the rustlers. They eyed Rat with a new sense of appreciation. But the truth of the matter is that even the old hands had always found it difficult to become accustomed to a rattlesnake in camp.

It was Three-fingered Ike who gave voice to the feelings of many of the hands. "That rattler never seems to do no harm, but somehow I jest cain't seem to git used to him."

"*Ni yo tampoco,*" said Cuchillos y Agudos.

"Me neither," said Gun Smith. "But no rattlesnake seems to bother Bill none. Why, only last night when we was camped, he done something that I never seen before."

"What was that?" asked Cherry.

Bill, returning from night guard, stepped into the circle of light thrown out by the campfire.

Gun looked up. "I was jest goin' to tell the boys about what happened last night." He turned back to his audience. "Well, sir, we had turned in. I was sleepin' sound. All of a sudden, I woke up. I didn't know what it was. But somethin' woke me. I was lyin' there, tryin' to find out what it was. And I turned my eyes over to where Bill was layin'."

"Oh yes," said Pecos, "I remember." A smile spread over his face as he recalled the incident. He took up the thread of the story. "I was jest about dozin' off when . . ."

The thread was cut short. "I tell you," Gun Smith interrupted, "I never seen such a thing. There was Bill a-layin' and perched right on top of his chest, all coiled up as nice as you please, was a big rattler!"

"He jest crawled up there to spend the night," said Pecos defensively.

"Shore. First, I thought it was Rat. But it wasn't Rat. Rat was curled up around the rim of Bill's hat, with his tail in one of Bill's boots to keep it warm, jest like he always does. Then, of course, I know'd this was another rattler. A wild one. I jest didn't know what to do. I figgered fer a minute I better shoot him. But then a feller might git into trouble shootin' a gun off that close to Pecos. I was some troubled fer a minute. Then I seen that Bill was awake, too. He jest woke up."

"Now Gun," Pecos broke in, "I know you're a stickler fer tellin' an honest story, and you want all the facts truthful and correct."

"Why, shore."

"The truth is I had been dozin'. 'Bout half asleep. But I had woke up jest before that. When he first crawled up there, to tell the truth."

"What happened?" Cherry inquired.

The red embers glowing under the ashes of the campfire cast their soft light on Gun's bearded face, bringing into clear relief the rough, trustworthy, weatherworn features. The frankness and the simple honesty of the man were evident.

"I didn't know if he seen the snake or not," Gun continued. "Thinks I, I'll git a club. But then, how kin I club a rattler that's sittin' right there on Bill's chest. Jest coilin' up an' gittin' ready to go to sleep."

"Gun, I guess you ain't never goin' to git over that," said Bill, smiling.

"No sir, I ain't. I kin tell you I ain't!"

"I'm goin' to have some trouble gittin' over that myself," said Pretty Pete Rogers.

"It's all real simple," Pecos said. "The poor critter was cold. And he found a warm place to sleep on my chest."

"But Señor Beel!" Cuchillos exploded.

"Of course, I could have chased the rattler away. But if I did, he probably would have bit me."

"But rattler bites don't seem to harm you none. Leastways, you ain't afeard of 'em," said Curly Joe.

Pecos stretched lazily. Then he turned to Joe. "Don't fergit that if he'd a bit me, why, I would of had to bite him right back. Everything was so nice an' peaceful that I didn't want to start no argument. I never like to argue if I kin avoid it. Anyway, like I say, the pore snake was only cold."

Bill strolled to the bed wagon and pulled down his bedroll. The other cowpunchers followed his lead and prepared for sleep. After they were in their blankets and settled down for the night, Pretty Pete Rogers broke the silence.

"Bill, this-here is a wild country," he said. "It's jest filled with animals that ain't what you might call friendly. Some of 'em is jest plain loco. An' they run all the ways from centipedes to grizzly bears. There is lots of danger around. All the hands gits laid up at one time or another with some kind of misfortune or accident."

"Yep," replied Bill. "What you say is true. A man has got to look sharp and be real keerful all the time."

"What I cain't understand, Bill, is why you don't never seem to git in no accidents."

"I guess I never thought much about that."

"Ain't you never had no narrer escapes?"

"Nope. I reckon not," said Bill.

"You hunted bars, ain't you?" asked Pete.

"Yep."

"An' you hunted 'em with your bare hands, too? Without no guns?"

"Yep."

"An' you cain't remember no narrer escapes?"
Pete demanded.

"Oh, shore. Lots of narrer escapes," Bill agreed.
"But I didn't have 'em. The bars did."

Alkali Ike turned restlessly in his soogans. There
was a pause. The campfire flickered low.

Pete spoke again, "Jest think it over now. Real
keerful. Ain't you never had an accident, Bill?"

"Wal now . . ."

"Ain't a hoss never bucked you off?"

"Wal, no. I guess not."

"Ain't you never bin shot?"

"No. I reckon I ain't."

"Look here, Pecos," came the insistent voice out
of the darkness, "you must have bin in an accident
of some kind."

"Reckon not."

There was another pause. Gun Smith's voice broke
the silence. "I remember once, Bill, you told me you
was bit by a mountain lion. When you was a kid."

"Oh, that. Yep. That's right," said Pecos Bill.
"Only that wasn't no accident. The critter bit me on
purpose." Pecos Bill had the last word. There were
no more questions and silence settled down on the
sleepy camp.